REVISE M1

for MEI Structured Mathematics

D0185436

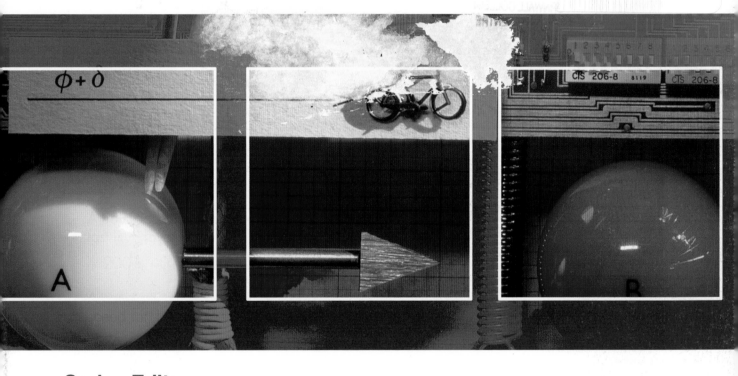

Series Editor
Roger Porkess

Authors
Pat Bryden, David Holland,
Maureen Sheehan, David Smart

HODDER
EDUCATION
AN HACHETTE UK COMPANY

Every effort has been made to trace all copyright holders, but if any have been inadvertently overlooked the Publishers will be pleased to make the necessary arrangements at the first opportunity.

Although every effort has been made to ensure that website addresses are correct at time of going to press, Hodder Education cannot be held responsible for the content of any website mentioned in this book. It is sometimes possible to find a relocated web page by typing in the address of the home page for a website in the URL window of your browser.

Hachette's policy is to use papers that are natural, renewable and recyclable products and made from wood grown in sustainable forests. The logging and manufacturing processes are expected to conform to the environmental regulations of the country of origin.

Orders: please contact Bookpoint Ltd, 130 Milton Park, Abingdon, Oxon OX14 4SB.
Telephone: (44) 01235 827720. Fax: (44) 01235 400454. Lines are open 9.00 – 5.00, Monday to Saturday, with a 24-hour message answering service.
Visit our website at www.hoddereducation.co.uk

© Pat Bryden, David Holland, Maureen Sheehan, David Smart, Roger Porkess, 2008
First published in 2008 by
Hodder Education,
an Hachette UK Company
338 Euston Road
London NW1 3BH

Impression number   5 4 3
Year   2013 2012

Dynamic Learning Student Online website © Pat Bryden, David Holland, Maureen Sheehan, David Smart, Roger Porkess, 2008; with contributions from Danielle Veall; developed by Infuze Limited; cast: Tom Frankland, Gina Walker; recorded at Alchemy Soho.

Typeset in 11/12 Helvetica by Tech-Set Ltd., Gateshead, Tyne & Wear
Printed in India

A catalogue record for this title is available from the British Library

ISBN: 978 0 340 95740 0

Contents

Introduction

Welcome to this Revision Guide for the MEI Mechanics 1 unit!

The book is organised into 17 sections covering the various topics in the syllabus. They follow essentially the same order as the textbook. A typical section is four pages long; the first three pages contain essential information and key worked examples covering the topic.

The last page in each section has questions for you to answer so that you can be sure that you have really understood the topic. There is a multiple-choice exercise and an exam-style question. If you are to gain the greatest possible benefit from the book, and so do your best in the Mechanics 1 exam, you should work through these for yourself and then refer to the accompanying website to check your answers.

The multiple-choice questions cover the basic ideas and techniques. It is really important that you work through them carefully; guessing will do you no good at all. When you have decided on the answer you think is right, enter it on the website. If you are right, it tells you so and gives the full solution; check that your answer wasn't just a fluke. If your choice is not right, the website gives you advice about your mistake; the possible wrong answers have all been designed to pick out particular common misunderstandings. The explanations on the website are based on the most likely mistakes; even if you make a different mistake, you will usually find enough help to set you on the right path so that you can try again.

When you come onto the exam-style question, write out your best possible answer. Then go to the website. You will find the solution displayed step-by-step, together with someone talking you through it and giving you helpful advice.

So the book contains the essential information to revise for the exam and, critically, also enables you to check that you have understood it properly. That is a recipe for success.

Finally, a word of warning. This book is designed to be used together with the textbook and not as a replacement for it. This Revision Guide will help you to prepare for the exam but to do really well you also need the deep understanding that comes from the detailed explanations you will find in the textbook.

Good learning and good luck!

Pat Bryden, David Holland, Maureen Sheehan, David Smart, Roger Porkess

Where you see the following icon **ƆL**, please refer to the Dynamic Learning Student Online website. Information on how to access this website is printed on the inside front cover of this book.

Accompanying books

MEI Structured Mathematics Mechanics 1
ISBN 978 0 340 81400 0

Companion to Advanced Mathematics and Statistics
ISBN 978 0 340 95923 7

Motion

Nomenclature, vectors, scalars and signs

A ABOUT THIS TOPIC

This section introduces some of the key terms and concepts involved in the study of motion (known as *kinematics*). The important distinction between a vector quantity and a scalar quantity is also highlighted.

R REMEMBER

- The terms *time*, *distance* and *speed* from GCSE.
- Knowledge of graphical techniques from GCSE.
- Basic algebra from GCSE.

K KEY FACTS

VECTORS (have magnitude and direction)
Displacement
Position – displacement from a fixed origin
Velocity – rate of change of position
*Acceleration** – rate of change of velocity

SCALARS (have magnitude only)
Distance

Speed – magnitude of velocity

Time

* Warning: although acceleration is strictly a vector, it is commonly used as a scalar

Definitions

- Average speed $= \dfrac{\text{total distance travelled}}{\text{total time taken}}$ (it is a scalar quantity)

- Average velocity $= \dfrac{\text{displacement}}{\text{time taken}}$ (it is a vector quantity)

- Average acceleration $= \dfrac{\text{change in velocity}}{\text{time}}$ (it is a vector quantity)

Graphs

- *Position–time*
- *Velocity–time*

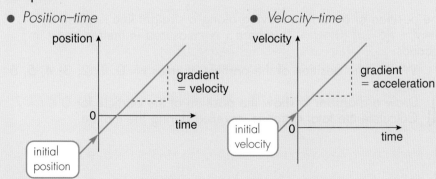

EXAMPLE 1

The motion of a particle is illustrated by the position–time graph below.
i) Describe what is happening during these six seconds.
ii) Sketch a graph of distance travelled against time.

SOLUTION

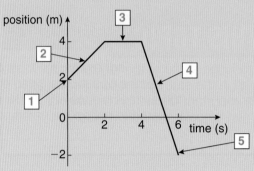

i) The five key elements of the motion during these six seconds are:
1. The particle starts 2 m from the origin.
2. The particle moves away from the origin with a constant speed ('constant' as the line is straight) of $1 \, m \, s^{-2}$ (the gradient of the line is $\frac{2}{2} = 1 \, m \, s^{-1}$) for 2 s; it travels 2 m.
3. For the next 2 s the particle remains at 4 m from the origin, so is stationary.
4. The particle moves in the **opposite** direction with a constant speed of $3 \, m \, s^{-1}$ for 2 s, so the velocity is $-3 \, m \, s^{-1}$ (the gradient of the line is -3).
5. The particle ends up 2 m the other side of the origin.
ii) The first section is a line is from $(0, 0)$ to $(2, 2)$
followed by a line from $(2, 2)$ to $(4, 2)$
and finally a line from $(4, 2)$ to $(6, 8)$.

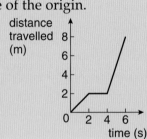

EXAMPLE 2

The position of a particle moving along a straight line is given by
$x = 7 + t(6 - t)$ $(0 \leq t \leq 7)$, where x is measured in metres and t in seconds.
i) What is the position of the particle at times $t = 0, 1, 2, 3, 4, 5, 6$ and 7?
ii) Draw a diagram to show the position of the particle for $0 \leq t \leq 7$.
iii) Calculate the total distance travelled during the motion.

i)

t	0	1	2	3	4	5	6	7
x	7	12	15	16	15	12	7	0

ii)

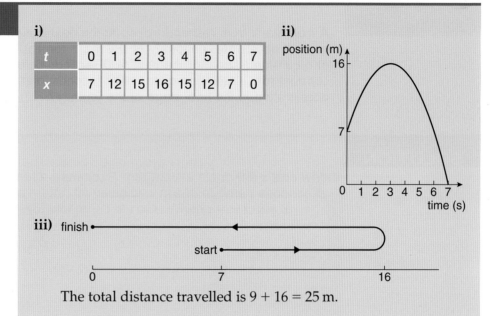

iii)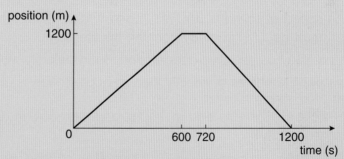

The total distance travelled is $9 + 16 = 25$ m.

EXAMPLE 3

Jack takes 10 minutes to walk 1200 m, at a constant rate, in a westerly direction. He rests for 2 minutes before taking another 8 minutes to return to his starting point, again walking at a constant rate.
i) Sketch a graph of position against time.
ii) Calculate his average speed for the whole journey.
iii) Calculate his average velocity for the whole journey.

---

i) Take the origin as his starting point, west as the positive direction and the unit of time as a second. As Jack walks at a constant rate, each section of the graph will be a straight line.

ii) Average speed $= \dfrac{\text{total distance travelled}}{\text{total time taken}}$

So his average speed $= \dfrac{1200 + 1200}{600 + 120 + 480} = \dfrac{2400}{1200} = 2 \, \text{m s}^{-1}$

iii) Average velocity $= \dfrac{\text{displacement}}{\text{time taken}}$

> He walks 1200 m, and then walks back to his starting point.

The displacement for the whole journey is 0 m (west)

So his average velocity $= \dfrac{0}{1200} = 0 \, \text{m s}^{-1}$ (west)

EXAMPLE 4

A train starts from rest and travels to the next station along a straight track. It accelerates uniformly at $0.2 \, \mathrm{m \, s^{-2}}$ for 150 seconds, then travels at a constant speed for the next 600 seconds before slowing down at a constant rate, coming to a stop 100 seconds later. What is the acceleration in the final stage of the journey?

SOLUTION

 LINKS

Mechanics
The ideas of this section are fundamental to all work on motion, so will be relevant to much of the work on mechanics which you will meet.

As acceleration $= \dfrac{\text{change in velocity}}{\text{time}}$

Start by finding the maximum velocity v for the first stage of the journey, as you will need to know this to work out the change in velocity for the final stage in the journey.

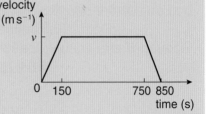

$0.2 = \dfrac{v - 0}{150}$

$\therefore v = 30$

So the final acceleration $= \dfrac{\text{change in velocity}}{\text{time}} = \dfrac{0 - 30}{100} = -0.3 \, \mathrm{m \, s^{-2}}$

Note that this acceleration is **negative** as the train is slowing down.

Test Yourself ▷L

1 Which one of the following statements is true?

  A The speed of light is $3 \times 10^8 \, \mathrm{m \, s^{-1}}$ and the mean distance from the sun to the earth is $1.5 \times 10^8 \, \mathrm{km}$, so it takes $0.5 \, \mathrm{s}$ for light to reach the earth from the sun.

  B The speed of sound is $340 \, \mathrm{m \, s^{-1}}$ and it takes $5 \, \mathrm{s}$ for the sound of thunder to reach me, so I must be $1.7 \, \mathrm{km}$ away from the thunderstorm.

  C A particle has negative acceleration, so its velocity must also be negative.

  D If a particle has zero velocity then its acceleration is also zero.

2 Alan walks 300 m due east in 150 s, and then 150 m due west in 50 s. What is his average velocity?

  A $2.25 \, \mathrm{m \, s^{-1}}$ B $0.75 \, \mathrm{m \, s^{-1}}$

  C $2.25 \, \mathrm{m \, s^{-1}}$ east   D $0.75 \, \mathrm{m \, s^{-1}}$ east

3 The quantities in one of the following groups are either all scalars or all vectors. In the other groups there are some of each. In which group are all the quantities the same type?

  A distance, velocity, acceleration   B time, displacement, speed

  C time, speed, distance   D position, speed, acceleration

4 The position of a particle moving along a straight line is given by $x = 5 + 4t - t^2$, where x is measured in metres and t in seconds. What is the distance travelled between $t = 0$ and $t = 5$?

  A $-5 \, \mathrm{m}$ B $5 \, \mathrm{m}$

  C $9 \, \mathrm{m}$ D $13 \, \mathrm{m}$

Exam-Style Question ⊃L

A shuttle train travels along a straight track between two stations A and B, which are 2.1 km apart. On leaving one station, the train accelerates uniformly at 0.1 m s^{-2} and covers 500 m in 100 s before reaching its maximum speed of $v \text{ m s}^{-1}$. It then travels at a constant speed before beginning to slow down uniformly in order to stop at the other station. This final phase takes 80 s, during which time the train covers 400 m.

i) A) Calculate the maximum speed, $v \text{ m s}^{-1}$.

    B) How long does it take for the journey from A to B? What is the average speed of the journey from A to B?

    C) What is the acceleration during the final phase of the journey?

ii) A) Draw a velocity–time graph of the journey from A to B and back to A, assuming that the train stops for 3 minutes at station B and that, on the return journey, the pattern of motion is the same as when it is travelling from A to B.

    B) What is the average velocity for the journey from A to B and back to A?

Motion: using graphs

The section develops the ideas introduced in the last section by concentrating on the use of position–time, velocity–time, distance–time, speed–time and acceleration–time graphs.

- The terms *time*, *distance* and *speed* from GCSE.
- Knowledge of graphical techniques from GCSE.
- Basic algebra from GCSE.
- The gradient of a line from GCSE.
- The formula for calculating the area of a trapezium from GCSE.
- Quadratic equations from GCSE and C1.

Definitions (for motion in a straight line)
- *Displacement* – the distance and direction of one point from another (a vector)
- *Position* – the displacement from the origin (a vector)
- *Distance travelled* – the length of the path travelled, whatever the direction (a scalar)

Graphs
- *Position–time*
- *Velocity–time*
- *Distance–time*
- *Speed–time*

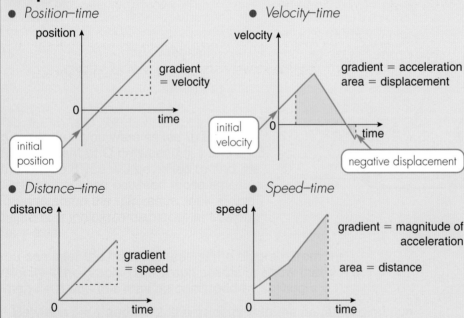

EXAMPLE 1

A heavy goods train starts from rest and accelerates uniformly for 120 s, by which time its speed is $12 \, \text{m s}^{-1}$. It travels at this speed for the next 600 s and then decelerates uniformly, coming to rest 80 s later.
i) Sketch the speed–time graph.
ii) What is the acceleration of the train during the final stage of its journey?
iii) Find the total distance travelled.

SOLUTION

i)

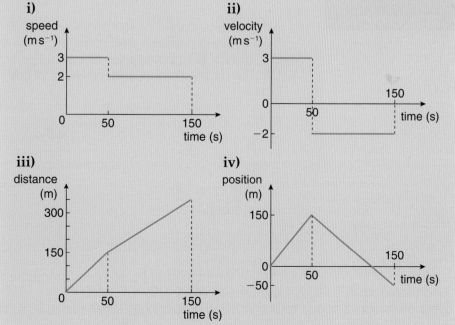

ii) The acceleration during the final stage of the journey
= gradient of BC
$$= \frac{-12}{80} = -0.15 \, \text{m s}^{-2}$$

> ⚠ Note that the acceleration is **negative** as the train is slowing down.

iii) The distance travelled is found by calculating the area under the speed–time graph, that is the area of the trapezium OABC.
$$\text{Area} = \tfrac{1}{2}(800 + 600) \times 12 = 8400$$

> Trapezium area = $\tfrac{1}{2}$(OC + AB) × height

The distance travelled is 8400 m = 8.4 km.

EXAMPLE 2

Jane walks north for 50 s at 3 m s⁻¹ and then south for 100 s at 2 m s⁻¹. Sketch
i) the speed–time graph
ii) the velocity–time graph
iii) the distance–time graph
iv) the position–time graph.

SOLUTION

Choose the origin as Jane's starting point and north as the positive direction.

i)

speed (m s⁻¹) vs time (s)

ii)

velocity (m s⁻¹) vs time (s)

iii)

distance (m) vs time (s)

iv)

position (m) vs time (s)

Jane covers a total distance of 350 m.

Jane ends up 50 m south of her starting point.

EXAMPLE 3

A train takes 5 minutes to travel between two stations which are 2 km apart. The train accelerates for 60 s before reaching its maximum speed. It then travels at this speed before being brought to rest in 40 s with a constant deceleration. What is the maximum speed of the train?

SOLUTION

The sketch of the speed–time graph of the journey shows the given information, with suitable units.
The maximum speed is v m s^{-1}.

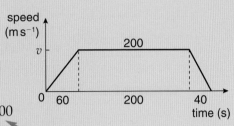

The area is $\frac{1}{2}(300 + 200) \times v = 2000$

> The area of the trapezium equals the total distance travelled, which is 2 km or 2000 m.

$$\Rightarrow v = \frac{2000}{250} = 8$$

The maximum speed of the train is 8 m s^{-1}.

EXAMPLE 4

The velocity–time graph illustrates the progress of a car along a straight road during a two minute period.
i) Describe the car's journey.
ii) Draw the acceleration–time graph.
iii) How far does the car travel?

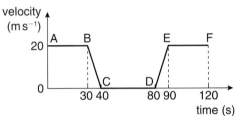

SOLUTION

i) **AB**: the car travels at a steady velocity of 20 m s^{-1} for 30 s
   BC: the car decelerates uniformly to a stop in 10 s
   CD: the car is stationary for 40 s
   DE: the car accelerates uniformly for 10 s reaching a velocity of 20 m s^{-1}
   EF: the car travels at a steady velocity of 20 m s^{-1} for 30 s.

ii) In AB, CD and EF the acceleration is 0 m s^{-2}.
   In BC the acceleration is $\frac{-20}{10} = -2$ m s^{-2}.
   In DE the acceleration is $\frac{20}{10} = 2$ m s^{-2}.

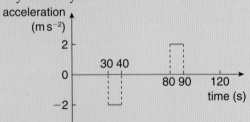

iii) The displacement of the car, which is the same as the actual distance it travels as the velocity is not negative at any stage during the two minutes, is found by calculating the area under the velocity–time graph.
   The velocity–time graph is symmetrical, so the
   area $= \frac{1}{2}(30 + 40) \times 20 \times 2 = 1400$.
   The distance travelled is 1400 m.

LINKS

Mechanics
The ideas in this section are fundamental to all work on motion, so will be relevant to most of the topics you will meet.

Test Yourself

1 The driver of a car, which has been stopped at traffic lights, finds that she is then stopped at the next traffic lights. Which of the following graphs could represent the velocity–time graph for the car as it travels between the two sets of traffic lights?

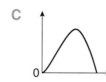

2 A particle moves in a straight line from A to C, passing through B. It starts from rest at A and accelerates uniformly at $1 \, m \, s^{-2}$ for 5 s before arriving at B. Between B and C it accelerates uniformly at $2 \, m \, s^{-2}$ for another 5 s. Draw the speed–time graph for this motion and then answer the following question. What is the average speed of the particle in its journey from A to C?

 A $6\frac{2}{3} \, m \, s^{-1}$ B $3.75 \, m \, s^{-1}$ C $1.5 \, m \, s^{-1}$ D $6.25 \, m \, s^{-1}$

3 A body travels in a straight line. It accelerates uniformly from rest at $0.4 \, m \, s^{-2}$, then travels at a constant speed of $8 \, m \, s^{-1}$, after which it is brought to rest with a constant retardation. It travels 600 m in 100 s. Which of the following statements is true?

 A The magnitude of the retardation is $0.4 \, m \, s^{-2}$.

 B The body travels at a constant speed for 50 s.

 C The body travels half the distance in half the time.

 D If the acceleration had been $0.8 \, m \, s^{-2}$ instead of $0.4 \, m \, s^{-2}$ the body would have travelled for longer at a constant speed.

4 A particle, which starts from rest, travels along a straight line. Its acceleration during the time interval $0 \leqslant t \leqslant 10$ is given by this acceleration–time graph.
When is the speed of the particle greatest?

 A $t = 4$ B $4 \leqslant t \leqslant 7$

 C $t = 9$ D $t = 10$

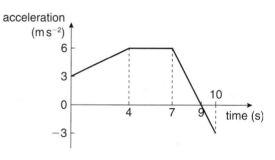

Exam-Style Question

P and Q are two points 700 m apart on a straight road. A car passes the point P with a speed of $8 \, m \, s^{-1}$ and immediately accelerates uniformly, reaching a top speed of $28 \, m \, s^{-1}$ in 5 s. The driver continues at this speed for another 15 s before decelerating uniformly for T seconds at $1.8 \, m \, s^{-2}$ until he reaches Q. When the car passes Q its speed is $V \, m \, s^{-1}$.

i)   Sketch the speed–time graph for the journey between P and Q.

ii) A) Find the acceleration.
     B) Calculate the distance of the car from P when the top speed is reached.

iii) Find the values of T and V.

iv) A) Find the average speed for the journey between P and Q.
     B) Draw the acceleration–time graph for the journey from P to Q.

Modelling using constant acceleration 2

Constant acceleration equations

K **KEY FACTS**

The *suvat* equations

- The equations for motion with **constant** acceleration are

  ① $v = u + at$ 　　　　　　② $s = \frac{1}{2}(u + v)t$

  ③ $s = ut + \frac{1}{2}at^2$ 　　　　④ $v^2 = u^2 + 2as$

  ⑤ $s = vt - \frac{1}{2}at^2$

  a is the constant acceleration;
  s is the displacement from the starting position at time t;
  v is the velocity at time t;
  u is the initial velocity (when $t = 0$).

- a and u have the same value throughout the motion. s and v vary as t varies.

The *suvat* equations are obtained by assuming that the velocity–time graph is a straight line, as shown here.

The gradient is the acceleration and this is constant.

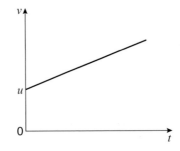

Remember not to use the *suvat* equations unless you are sure the acceleration is constant.

EXAMPLE 1

A bus accelerates from rest to $13\,\mathrm{m\,s^{-1}}$ in 6 seconds. Assuming the acceleration is constant, how far does it travel in this time?

SOLUTION

First decide which equation to use.
You know that $u = 0$, $v = 13$, and $t = 6$. You need s.
Choose $s = \frac{1}{2}(u + v)t$
Now substitute the values you know:
$$s = \frac{1}{2}(0 + 13) \times 6$$
Distance travelled $= 39\,\mathrm{m}$

In this question you were told the speed of the bus in $\mathrm{m\,s^{-1}}$ so the units were compatible. If you had been told the speed in m.p.h., you would have had to convert this to $\mathrm{m\,s^{-1}}$ before using it.

 Always make sure your units are compatible.

EXAMPLE 2

Calculate the constant acceleration in example 1.

SOLUTION

Now you know $u = 0$, $v = 13$ and $t = 6$, and you need a.
Choose $v = u + at$
$$13 = 0 + a \times 6 \quad \longleftarrow \boxed{\text{Substituting the values you know.}}$$
$$a = 13 \div 6$$
The acceleration is $2.17\,\mathrm{m\,s^{-2}}$ (to 3 s.f.).

EXAMPLE 3

Starting at $25\,\mathrm{m\,s^{-1}}$, a car slows down (decelerates) at $2\,\mathrm{m\,s^{-2}}$.
i) How long does it take to stop?
ii) How long does it take to travel $100\,\mathrm{m}$ from its starting point?

SOLUTION

i) A deceleration (or retardation) of $2\,\mathrm{m\,s^{-2}}$ is an acceleration of $-2\,\mathrm{m\,s^{-2}}$.
    You know $u = 25$, $v = 0$, $a = -2$ and you need t.
    Choose $v = u + at$
    $$0 = 25 - 2t \quad \longleftarrow \boxed{\text{Substituting the known values.}}$$
    $$2t = 25$$
    The time it takes to stop is $12.5\,\mathrm{s}$.

ii) Now you know $u = 25$, $a = -2$ and $s = 100$, and you need t.
    Choose $s = ut + \frac{1}{2}at^2$
    Giving $100 = 25t - 1t^2$
    Rearranging $t^2 - 25t + 100 = 0 \quad \longleftarrow \boxed{\text{Solve this quadratic by factorising.}}$
    $$(t - 5)(t - 20) = 0$$
    $$t = 5 \text{ or } t = 20$$

    $\boxed{\text{The car had stopped after } 12.5 \text{ seconds so } t = 20 \text{ is rejected.}}$

    The answer is that the car takes 5 seconds to travel $100\,\mathrm{m}$.

EXAMPLE 4

A car travels along a straight road ABC. AB is 27 m and BC is 100 m. The car starts from rest at A, accelerates uniformly at $1.5 \, \text{m s}^{-2}$ to B and then travels at constant velocity to C. How long does this total journey take?

SOLUTION

Start by putting the information on a diagram.

> There are two parts to the motion so use
> $u_1, v_1, s_1, t_1, a_1,$ for A to B and
> $u_2, v_2, s_2, t_2, a_2,$ for B to C.
> Notice that $v_1 = u_2,$ the velocity at B.

A $a_1 = 1.5$ B $a_2 = 0$ C

$s_1 = 27$
$t_1 = ?$

$s_2 = 100$
$t_2 = ?$

$u_1 = 0$ $v_1 = u_2 = ?$ $v_2 = u_2$

First find the time, t_1 s, taken to accelerate between A and B.

Use $s = ut + \tfrac{1}{2}at^2$

> You know $s_1 = 27, u_1 = 0$ and $a_1 = 1.5$; you need t_1.

$27 = 0 + \tfrac{1}{2} \times 1.5 \times t_1^2$

$t_1^2 = 2 \times 27 \div 1.5$

$t_1 = \sqrt{36} = 6$ ← Remember the square root.

For the second stage, from B to C, you need the constant speed. This is the value of v at B, the end of the first stage.

Using $v^2 = u^2 + 2as$

> You know $u_1 = 0, a_1 = 1.5$ and $s_1 = 27$; you need v_1.

$v_1^2 = 0 + 2 \times 1.5 \times 27$

$v_1 = \sqrt{81} = 9$

The time taken at constant speed equals distance ÷ speed, that is $s_2 \div v$

so $t_2 = 100 \div 9$
$= 11\tfrac{1}{9}$

The total time taken is $t_1 + t_2 = 6 + 11\tfrac{1}{9}$
$= 17.1 \, \text{s}$ (to 3 s.f.).

⚠ • For the second part of example 4, you could have used $v = u + at$ with your answer for t_1 to find v, but a mistake in t_1 would have led to another mistake in v. It is better to use the information given in the question if you can.

• Remember that s is not the same as the distance travelled if the direction changes during the motion.

LINKS

Pure Mathematics   Solution of simultaneous and quadratic equations (C1).
Mechanics   Vertical motion under gravity (M1), Projectile motion (with constant acceleration as a special case) (M1), Applying Newton's second law of motion along a line and in two dimensions (M1), General motion (M1).

Test Yourself ⊃L

Before you start these questions, cover **question 1** and write down the following *suvat* equations from memory. Do all of them before you check your answers.
Make sure you learn any you get wrong and try this test again after doing **question 1**.

i) An equation involving s, t, u, v
ii) An equation involving a, t, u, v
iii) An equation involving a, s, u, v
iv) An equation involving a, s, t, v
v) An equation involving a, s, t, u

1 For each of the following decide which *single* equation is the most appropriate.

$\quad$ **A** $v = u + at$ $\qquad$ **B** $s = \frac{1}{2}(u + v)t$ $\qquad$ **C** $s = ut + \frac{1}{2}at^2$ $\qquad$ **D** $v^2 = u^2 + 2as$

$\quad$ **i)** A van travelling at $12\,\text{m s}^{-1}$ stops in $4\,\text{s}$. How far does it travel in that time?
$\quad$ **ii)** A bus stops in a distance of $100\,\text{m}$ from a speed of $10\,\text{m s}^{-1}$. What is its acceleration?
$\quad$ **iii)** A ball is dropped from a window at a height of $15\,\text{m}$ and accelerates at $9.8\,\text{m s}^{-2}$. How long does it take to reach the ground?
$\quad$ **iv)** What is the speed of the ball in part **iii)** when it has fallen $10\,\text{m}$?

2 A light aircraft lands with a speed of $30\,\text{m s}^{-1}$ and takes 20 seconds to come to rest. Assuming constant acceleration, three of the following statements are true and one is false. Which one is false?

$\quad$ **A** The aeroplane travels $300\,\text{m}$ before coming to rest.
$\quad$ **B** The acceleration of the aeroplane is $-1.5\,\text{m s}^{-2}$.
$\quad$ **C** The aeroplane travels half the distance in the first 10 seconds.
$\quad$ **D** The speed of the aeroplane is halved after 10 seconds.

3 A train accelerates from rest at $0.2\,\text{m s}^{-2}$ for $4000\,\text{m}$. How long does it take and how fast is it travelling?

$\quad$ **A** $200\,\text{s}, 40\,\text{m s}^{-1}$ $\qquad$ **B** $200\,\text{s}, 20\,\text{m s}^{-1}$ $\qquad$ **C** $20\,\text{s}, 40\,\text{m s}^{-1}$ $\qquad$ **D** $20\,\text{s}, 4\,\text{m s}^{-1}$

4 A car starts at rest and accelerates at $2\,\text{m s}^{-2}$ for 4 seconds. It then travels at constant speed for 10 minutes. How far has it travelled in this time?

$\quad$ **A** $76\,\text{m}$ $\qquad$ **B** $196\,\text{m}$ $\qquad$ **C** $4800\,\text{m}$ $\qquad$ **D** $4816\,\text{m}$

Exam-Style Question ⊃L

A car is travelling along a straight road with an initial speed of $11\,\text{m s}^{-1}$ when it starts to slow down at a traffic light. Its deceleration is constant. The car stops after 3 seconds, waits for 5 seconds and then accelerates uniformly to its original speed of $11\,\text{m s}^{-1}$ in 4 seconds.

i) Calculate the distance travelled by the car during these 12 seconds.

ii) How much less time would the car have taken to travel this distance if it had maintained a speed of $11\,\text{m s}^{-1}$ throughout the 12 seconds?

Vertical motion under gravity

K **KEY FACTS**

- The acceleration due to gravity ($g \, \text{m s}^{-2}$) is $9.8 \, \text{m s}^{-2}$ vertically downwards.

- $v = 0$ at the highest point of the motion.

- Always draw a diagram and decide in advance where your origin is and which way is positive. $s = 0$ is the origin. Whatever the position, v is positive in the positive direction. a is $+9.8$ when downwards is positive and -9.8 when upwards is positive.

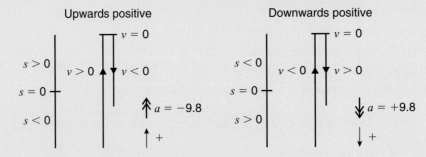

- In problems where the motion does not begin at the origin, that is $s = s_0$ when $t = 0$, replace s in each of the *suvat* equations with $(s - s_0)$.

EXAMPLE 1

A ball is projected upwards at $4.9 \, \text{m s}^{-1}$.
i) Find the time it takes to reach its maximum height.
ii) Find the actual maximum height.

SOLUTION

i) The ball reaches its maximum height when its velocity is zero.
First you need to find the time this occurs.
Take upwards as positive and $t = 0$ when it is projected.
You know $u = 4.9$, $a = -9.8$ and $v = 0$; you need t.
Choose $v = u + at$

$$0 = 4.9 + (-9.8)t$$
$$9.8t = 4.9$$
$$t = 0.5$$

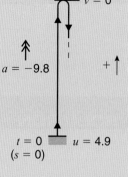

ii) Now take $s = 0$ when $t = 0$.
To find the maximum height, you need s when $t = 0.5$.
$u = 4.9$, $t = 0.5$, $a = -9.8$; you need s.
Choose $s = ut + \frac{1}{2}at^2$

$$s = 4.9 \times 0.5 + \frac{1}{2} \times (-9.8) \times (0.5)^2$$
$$= 2.45 - 1.225 = 1.225$$

The maximum height is 1.23 m (3 s.f.).

EXAMPLE 2

A ball is projected vertically upwards from a height of 1 m and reaches its maximum height after 2 seconds. Find
i) the initial velocity of the ball
ii) the velocity of the ball when it hits the ground.

SOLUTION

i) Take upwards to be positive.
You know $v = 0$ when $t = 2$ and $a = -9.8$, and you are asked to find u.
Choose $v = u + at$

$$0 = u - 9.8 \times 2$$
$$u = 19.6$$

> You are asked for the velocity so you have to give both the speed (19.6 m s⁻¹) and the direction (upwards).

The initial velocity is 19.6 m s⁻¹ upwards.

ii) To find the velocity when the ball hits the ground, you need v when $s = -1$, assuming $s = 0$ when $t = 0$.
You also need to use the value of u that you have just found.
Choose $v^2 = u^2 + 2as$

$$v^2 = 19.6^2 + 2 \times (-9.8) \times (-1)$$
$$v^2 = 403.76$$
$$v = -\sqrt{403.76}$$
$$= -20.09\ldots$$

> v is negative means that the ball is moving downwards.

When the ball hits the ground it has a velocity of 20.1 m s⁻¹ downwards (3 s.f.).

 It is tempting to say that $v = 0$ when the ball hits the ground because it is likely to stop instantaneously even if it bounces. However, questions like this actually mean 'just before it hits the ground', so $v \neq 0$. The time when $v = 0$ is when the ball is at maximum height and so changes from going up to going down.

EXAMPLE 3

A ball is dropped from a height of 8 m, hits the ground and rebounds at half the speed. How high does it bounce?

> It is tempting to assume that the first bounce is half the height, but you might be wrong. It is important to work out the answer properly.

SOLUTION

First find the speed of the ball when it hits the ground.
- Take downwards to be positive.
- Take the point where it is dropped as origin.

You know $u = 0$, $a = 9.8$, $s = 8$ and want to find v.

Choose $v^2 = u^2 + 2as$
$$= 0 + 2 \times 9.8 \times 8$$
$$v = \sqrt{156.8}$$
$$= 12.521\ldots$$

> Keep this whole number in your calculator.

Rebound speed $= \frac{1}{2} \times 12.521\ldots = 6.26 \text{ m s}^{-1}$ (3 s.f.)

The ball is now travelling upwards, so for this part of the motion
- take upwards to be positive
- take the point where it bounced as the origin.

$u = 6.260\ldots$, $a = -9.8$, $v = 0$ and you need s.

Again, use $v^2 = u^2 + 2as$
$$0 = 6.260\ldots^2 - 2 \times 9.8s$$
$$19.6s = 39.2$$
$$s = 2 \text{ m}$$

> The bounce is 2 m, so if you thought the bounce would be half of 8 m you were not correct.

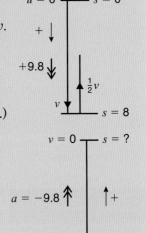

EXAMPLE 4

A ball is hit upwards and passes the top of a telegraph pole after 1.5 s and again after 2 s. Find its initial speed, u m s^{-1}, and the height of the pole, h m, above the point where the ball is hit.

SOLUTION

Take the ball's starting point to be the origin and upwards to be positive.
The two times when the ball passes the top of the pole are 1.5 s (on the way up) and 2 s (on the way down).

Now you only know a and two values of t. You are asked for u and h, so you will need two equations involving u and h.

$a = -9.8$, $t = 2$, $u = ?$, $s = h$

Choose $\qquad s = ut + \frac{1}{2}at^2$

On the way up: $\quad h = 1.5u + \frac{1}{2} \times (-9.8) \times 1.5^2$
$$h = 1.5u - 11.025 \qquad ①$$

On the way down: $h = 2u + \frac{1}{2} \times (-9.8) \times 2^2$
$$h = 2u - 19.6 \qquad ②$$

Solving equations ① and ② simultaneously gives:
$$2u - 19.6 = 1.5u - 11.025$$
$$0.5u = 19.6 - 11.025$$
$$u = 8.575 \times 2 = 17.15$$

Substituting in ② gives $h = 2 \times 17.15 - 19.6 = 14.7$

The initial speed is 17.2 m s^{-1} and the height of the pole is 14.7 m.

> You can use ① to check this answer.

EXAMPLE 5

A small ball is thrown vertically upwards from a height of 1 m and takes 2 seconds to reach its highest point, h m above its point of projection. How far above the ground is the greatest height?

SOLUTION

The diagram shows the path of the ball. Assume upwards is positive so the acceleration is $-g = -9.8\,\text{m s}^{-2}$.

At the top: $v = 0$, $t = 2$ and $s = h$.

You do not know u and you need h.

Choose $s = vt - \frac{1}{2}at^2$

Then $h = 0 - \frac{1}{2} \times (-9.8) \times 2^2$

$\qquad h = 19.6$

The height above the ground is
$h + 1\,\text{m} = 20.6\,\text{m}$

You can take s as the distance from the ground, but then $s = 1$ when $t = 0$ so the equation to use is $s = 1 + vt - \frac{1}{2}at^2$ or $s - 1 = vt - \frac{1}{2}at^2$. In this case $t = 2$ gives $s = 20.6$ directly.

Diagram labels: $t = 2$ — $v = 0$ ← Highest point; h m ↓ $a = -9.8$; $+$ ↑; s; 0 ← Measure $s = 0$ from here. ; 1 m

LINKS

Pure Mathematics	Solution of simultaneous and quadratic equations (C1).
Mechanics	Projectile motion (M1), General motion (constant acceleration motion as a special case) (M1).
Differential Equations	Motion with resistance (DE).

Test Yourself ▷L

The following information applies to **questions 1 to 3**.

A ball is thrown upwards from a window with a speed of $3\,\text{m s}^{-1}$ and lands on the ground 15 m below. Take downwards to be positive and the level outside the window from which the ball is thrown to be the origin.
Three of these statements are false and one is true. Which one is the true statement?

1 **A** The distance travelled by the ball before it lands is 15 m.

  B The displacement of the ball is positive when it is above the window.

  C The ball's velocity is $+10\,\text{m s}^{-1}$ at some point during the motion.

  D The velocity of the ball is negative when it is below the window.

2 Which one of the following equations gives the time, t, taken for the ball to reach the ground?

  A $4.9t^2 - 3t - 15 = 0$ **B** $4.9t^2 + 3t - 15 = 0$

  C $4.9t^2 + 3t + 15 = 0$ **D** $9.8t^2 - 3t - 15 = 0$

3 When you have solved the correct equation in **question 2** you can use the results and the symmetry of the motion to give you even more information. Three of the following statements are true and one is false. Solve the correct equation from **question 2** and use your answers to decide which one is false.

 A The ball is at maximum height at 1.04 s.

 B The ball is in the air for 2.08 s.

 C The ball reaches the ground 1.47 s after passing the window on the way down.

 D The ball passes the window on the way down 0.61 s after it was thrown up.

 Try to think of another way of working out the correct answer for each statement.

The following information applies to **questions 4 and 5**.

Starting from rest, a rocket is fired vertically upwards with acceleration $25 \, \text{m s}^{-2}$. After 0.8 seconds there is no more fuel so it continues to move freely under gravity.

4 Calculate the maximum height of the rocket.

   A 8 m   B 16 m   C 20.4 m   D 28.4 m

5 From the moment when the rocket has no more fuel, it takes T seconds to return to earth. Which of these is a correct equation for T?

   A $4.9T^2 - 20T - 8 = 0$ B $4.9T^2 + 20T - 8 = 0$

   C $4.9T^2 - 20T + 8 = 0$ D $4.9T^2 + 20T + 8 = 0$

Exam-Style Question ▷L

A particle, P, is projected vertically upwards at $21 \, \text{m s}^{-1}$ from a point O on the ground.

i) Calculate the maximum height of P.

When P is at its highest point, a second particle, Q, is projected upwards from O at $15 \, \text{m s}^{-1}$.

ii) Show that P and Q collide 1.5 seconds later and determine the height above the ground that this takes place.

Forces and Newton's laws of motion

3

Newton's laws of motion

A | ABOUT THIS TOPIC

This section introduces you to Newton's laws of motion which underlie all the work you do in Mechanics, so it is important that you should understand what they imply.

R | REMEMBER

- Displacement, velocity, acceleration and force — These are vectors so each one has a magnitude (size) and a direction.

- Mass, length, speed and time — These are scalars with magnitude only.
- Equations for motion with constant acceleration (*suvat* equations).

K | KEY FACTS

- **Newton's laws of motion**
  I Every object continues in a state of rest or uniform motion in a straight line unless it is acted on by a resultant force.
  II Resultant force = mass × acceleration or $\mathbf{F} = m\mathbf{a}$
  III When one object exerts a force on another there is always a reaction which is equal, and opposite in direction, to the acting force.

- **S.I. units**

length	metre	(m)
time	second	(s)
velocity	metres per second	(m s^{-1})
acceleration	metres per second per second	(m s^{-2})
mass	kilogram	(kg)
force	*newton*	(N)

  1 newton is the force required to give a mass of 1 kilogram an acceleration of $1\ \text{m s}^{-2}$. 1000 newtons = 1 kilonewton (kN)

- **Weight**
  The weight of an object is the force of gravity pulling it towards the centre of the earth. Weight = *mg* vertically downwards. The weight of an object is represented by one force acting through its centre of mass.

Newton's first law

When the forces on an object are balanced and have *no resultant* they are said to be *in equilibrium*. Newton's first law says that in that case the velocity does not change. The object could be stationary (at rest) or it could have constant velocity. Constant velocity means that both the magnitude and the direction of the velocity remain unchanged.

The object must have constant speed and must be moving in a straight line. Newton's first law is a special case of his second with both *F* and *a* equal to zero.

EXAMPLE 1

In each of the following cases state whether the forces on the object are in equilibrium.
i) A car is cruising along a straight motorway at 60 m.p.h.
ii) A cable car on a straight wire pulls in to its terminal.
iii) The minute hand on my watch rotates at a steady speed.
iv) A kestrel's eye is fixed as it hovers over the ground.

SOLUTION

 Take care **not** to assume that a body is necessarily at rest when the forces acting on it are said to be in equilibrium.

i) A cruising car is assumed to have a constant speed and the road is straight, so the forces on the car as a whole must be in equilibrium.
ii) The cable car must be slowing down as it pulls into the terminal so its speed is not constant. The forces are not in equilibrium.
iii) The minute hand is not travelling in a straight line so the forces are not in equilibrium.
iv) As a bird of prey, the kestrel needs a steady eye. When it is stationary the forces acting on it are in equilibrium.

Newton's second law

Whenever either its speed or its direction of motion changes, an object has an acceleration. It could be travelling in a straight line with variable speed, or moving with constant speed along a curve, or both speed and direction could be changing.

In order to produce any acceleration, there must be a resultant force acting on the object in the same direction as the acceleration. A force of 1 newton gives a mass of 1 kg an acceleration of 1 m s^{-2}. This results in the following important equation:

$$\mathbf{F} = m\mathbf{a}$$

Any object falling to earth has an acceleration of $g \text{ m s}^{-2}$ vertically downwards, so the force of gravity acting on it is mg N. This is its **weight**.

 We often talk of things weighing, say, a kilogram when really we mean the mass is 1 kilogram. A 1 kilogram bag of sugar, for example, has a mass of 1 kg and a weight of $1 \times g = 9.8$ N.

EXAMPLE 2

A 60 kg parachutist has reached terminal velocity so is falling at a constant speed. What is the air resistance acting on the parachutist?

SOLUTION

The parachutist is falling at a constant speed so, assuming this is in a straight line, the forces acting are in equilibrium. The air resistance, *R*, is equal to the weight of the parachutist, mg.

Air resistance $= 60 \times g$
$= 588$ N

EXAMPLE 3

When a force of 0.5 N is applied to a toy truck, it travels 2.5 m in 2 seconds. Calculate the mass of the truck, assuming it starts from rest and accelerates uniformly.

SOLUTION

You can calculate the mass of the truck using $F = ma$ if you first find the acceleration.

$$s = ut + \tfrac{1}{2}at^2$$

> You know $u = 0$, $s = 1.5$ and $t = 2$, so use this equation.

giving
$$2.5 = 0 + \tfrac{1}{2}a \times 2^2$$
$$2.5 = 2a$$
$$a = 1.25$$

Now use
$$F = ma$$
giving
$$0.5 = m \times 1.25$$
$$m = 0.5 \div 1.25 = 0.4$$

The mass of the truck is 0.4 kg.

Newton's third law

Apart from its weight, every mechanical force acting on an object is the result of its physical contact with something in the outside world. It could be air, water, a string or rod, or another solid object. For every force acting on an object, there is an equal and opposite force acting on whatever is producing that force. (This is true of gravity as well.) For every action, there is an equal and opposite reaction.

EXAMPLE 4

In each case, state whether the force of the person on the wall is equal to, less than or greater than the weight of the person.
i) You are sitting on a low wall with your feet on the ground.
ii) A small child is sitting on the wall with feet dangling.
iii) You jump down on to the wall.

SOLUTION

i) You are at rest so the forces acting on you are in equilibrium. These are your weight downwards and the upwards forces due to contact with the wall and also the ground. Hence the force of the wall on you must be less than your weight. The equal force you apply to the wall is therefore less than your weight.
ii) In this case there is no force on the ground, so the force on the wall is equal to the weight of the child.
iii) When you land, the upward force acting on you must be greater than your weight in order to slow you down. Hence the equal and opposite downward force on the wall must also be greater than your weight.

LINKS

Mechanics   Force diagrams (M1), Applying Newton's second law along a line (M1), Forces and motion in two dimensions (M1), Newton's laws, in particular Newton's second law, are used in all levels of mechanics (M2, M3, M4).

Differential Equations   Many differential equations are derived using Newton's second law (DE).

Test Yourself ⟩L

In each of **questions 1 to 5** decide whether, during the situation described, the forces acting on the object are in equilibrium.

A Always **B** Never **C** Some, but not all, of the time **D** There is insufficient information to tell.

1 A book is lying on a table.

2 A skydiver is in free fall before reaching terminal velocity.

3 A lift in Canary Wharf rises without stopping from ground level to the fiftieth floor.

4 A child is sitting in a car on a fairground roundabout which is rotating with constant speed.

5 A person is sitting on a bus.

6 Three of the following statements are true and one is false. Which one is false?

A You are in a lift. When it starts moving, the force between you and the floor is not equal to your weight.

B A 1.5 kg bag of rice has a weight of 14.7 N.

C When something is moving, there must be a force making it move.

D When you are sitting on a chair, the force on the seat of the chair is normally less than your weight.

Exam-Style Question ⟩L

i) A van travelling along a straight horizontal road starts from rest, and accelerates at a constant rate to $30 \, \text{m s}^{-1}$ in 15 seconds. Calculate its acceleration.

ii) The van has a mass of 2 tonnes. What force is required to make it accelerate at this rate?

iii) After travelling at a steady rate of $30 \, \text{m s}^{-1}$ for 2 minutes, the van slows down at a constant rate and stops in a further 20 seconds. What resultant forces act on the van during these two parts of its motion?

You should make it clear how you are using Newton's laws when answering this question.

Forces

A ABOUT THIS TOPIC

This section reminds you of the different types of mechanical force and the ways they are represented using diagrams. It is very important to be able to draw clear diagrams showing the magnitudes and directions of forces acting on particular objects.

R REMEMBER

- Forces are vectors. They can be represented by a magnitude (size) and a direction given by an arrow.

K KEY FACTS

- **Newton's first and third laws**

  I Every object continues in a state of rest or uniform motion in a straight line unless it is acted on by a resultant force.

  III When one object exerts a force on another there is always a reaction which is equal, and opposite in direction, to the acting force.

- **Types of force**

  i) Forces on an object due to contact with the surface of another.
  Friction **always** opposes any tendency to slide.
  The *normal reaction* is always perpendicular to the surfaces and to any friction.
  These are the two components of the reaction between the surfaces in contact.

  normal reaction

  friction

  direction of possible sliding

  ii) Forces in a joining rod or string.

  > The tension and compression forces shown act on the objects attached to the ends.

  tension

  thrust or compression (rod only)

  iii) A smooth light pulley changes the direction of the tension in a string.

  T   T

  iv) The horizontal forces on a wheeled vehicle are usually reduced to three possible forces.

  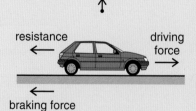

  resistance   driving force

  braking force

  v) The **weight** of an object is always directed vertically downwards and acts through the centre of mass of the object.

- **Commonly used modelling terms**

inextensible	does not vary in length	particle	negligible dimensions
light	negligible mass	smooth	negligible friction
negligible	small enough to ignore	uniform	the same throughout

EXAMPLE 1

Draw diagrams showing the forces acting on the following objects.
i) A computer mouse which is being moved along a table by a horizontal force P.
ii) The table due to the presence of the mouse.

SOLUTION

i) Forces on the mouse

normal reaction

P ← friction

weight

ii) Forces of mouse on table

Direction of motion

friction ← normal reaction

The friction and normal reaction forces acting on the table are equal and opposite to those of the table on the mouse.

- Notice that the weight of the mouse and the force P pushing it are present only in the diagram for the mouse.

- Because the mouse is moving horizontally, the normal reaction between it and the table is equal to its weight. However, the vertical reaction between any two objects is **not necessarily** equal to the weight of the one on top.

EXAMPLE 2

A girl attached to a rope is being lowered down a rock face. The rope passes through a smooth pulley at the top of the cliff and is held by a rock climber. The girl has her feet on a ledge and is momentarily at rest. Draw diagrams to show the forces acting on:
i) the girl
ii) the rock climber.

SOLUTION

i) Forces on the girl

M_1 is her mass.
T is the tension in the rope.
N_1 is the normal reaction of the ledge.
F_1 is the friction between her and the ledge.

ii) Forces on the rock climber

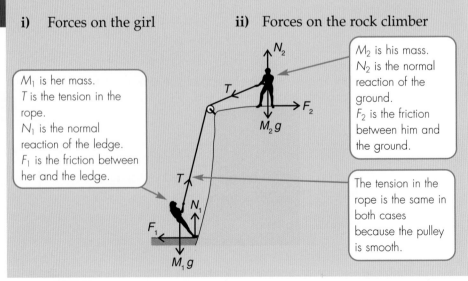

M_2 is his mass.
N_2 is the normal reaction of the ground.
F_2 is the friction between him and the ground.

The tension in the rope is the same in both cases because the pulley is smooth.

All forces are in newtons.

EXAMPLE 3

A tractor of mass 3000 kg is towing a trailer of mass 1000 kg at a steady speed along a straight horizontal road.
There is a driving force of 800 N.
There are also resistance forces of 500 N on the tractor and 300 N on the trailer.

i) Draw clearly labelled diagrams to show the forces on the tractor and on the trailer.

ii) Which of these forces are internal forces when the whole system is considered?

iii) Why is the driving force (800 N) equal to the sum of the resistances to motion (500 N + 300 N)?

iv) Find the vertical reaction forces and the tension in the towbar.

SOLUTION

> Notice that the **weights** of the tractor and trailer are each given as mg N.

i)

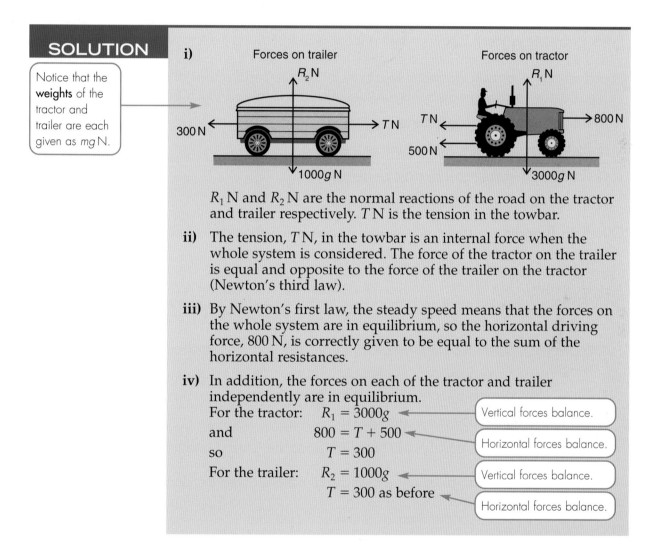

Forces on trailer $\qquad$ Forces on tractor

R_2 N $\qquad$ R_1 N

300 N $\qquad$ T N $\qquad$ T N $\qquad$ 800 N

500 N

1000g N $\qquad$ 3000g N

R_1 N and R_2 N are the normal reactions of the road on the tractor and trailer respectively. T N is the tension in the towbar.

ii) The tension, T N, in the towbar is an internal force when the whole system is considered. The force of the tractor on the trailer is equal and opposite to the force of the trailer on the tractor (Newton's third law).

iii) By Newton's first law, the steady speed means that the forces on the whole system are in equilibrium, so the horizontal driving force, 800 N, is correctly given to be equal to the sum of the horizontal resistances.

iv) In addition, the forces on each of the tractor and trailer independently are in equilibrium.

For the tractor: $\quad R_1 = 3000g$ $\qquad$ ← Vertical forces balance.

and $\qquad\qquad 800 = T + 500$ $\qquad$ ← Horizontal forces balance.

so $\qquad\qquad\quad T = 300$

For the trailer: $\quad R_2 = 1000g$ $\qquad$ ← Vertical forces balance.

$\qquad\qquad\quad T = 300$ as before $\qquad$ ← Horizontal forces balance.

LINKS

Mechanics $\quad$ Applying Newton's second law along a line (M1), Vectors (M1), Forces and motion in two dimensions (M1), General motion (M1). The work in this section underpins the later Mechanics units (M2, M3, M4).

CORNWALL COLLEGE
LEARNING CENTRE

Test Yourself

1 A small box is in equilibrium on a horizontal table. It is pulled by a string with tension T. Three of the following statements are true and one is false. Which one is false?

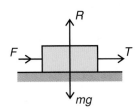

   A The friction force, F, is in the wrong direction.

   B R is the normal reaction of the table on the box.

   C $R = mg$

   D The magnitude of the tension, T, is greater than the magnitude of F.

2 A tractor is pulling a trailer with no brakes along level ground using a simple tow bar. The tractor brakes suddenly. Draw yourself a rough sketch showing the forces acting on the tractor and trailer at this moment (using the values in example 3 for the mass of the tractor and trailer, and resistance forces if you wish). Take care to indicate the directions of all the forces. Three of the following statements are true and one is false. Which one is false?

   A The forces are not in equilibrium.

   B The tractor and trailer slow down at the same rate.

   C The tension in the tow bar must be zero.

   D The braking force acts only on the tractor.

Questions 3 and 4 are about a boy who pushes a skateboard with his right foot whilst his left foot pushes against level ground. He is gaining speed.

3 One of the following statements must be true, the others may be false. Which one must be true?

   A The vertical reaction between the boy's right foot and the skateboard is equal to his weight.

   B There is a forwards frictional force on the boy's left foot.

   C The forces on the boy are in equilibrium.

   D The boy's weight is equally distributed between the ground and the skateboard.

4 Which of the following diagrams shows the directions of the frictional forces acting on the boy?
F_1 is the friction force of the ground on the boy's left foot.
F_2 is the friction force of the skateboard on the boy's right foot.

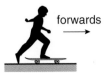

Exam-Style Question ▷L

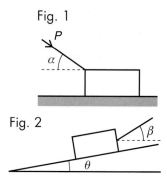

Fig. 1

Fig. 2

A student is moving a box of books of mass m kg to her lodgings.
First she pushes it along rough level ground with a force P N as shown
in Fig. 1.

i) Draw a diagram to show the forces acting on the box.
    Is the normal reaction with the ground equal to the weight of the box?

When the student reaches a ramp, she decides to pull the box with a rope,
making an angle of β to the horizontal as in Fig. 2. The ramp also is
rough and makes an angle of θ with the horizontal.

ii) Draw a diagram to show the forces now acting on the box.

Applying Newton's second law along a line

Newton's second law along a line

A ABOUT THIS TOPIC

This topic covers what you need to know in order to apply Newton's second law when forces act along the line of motion.

R REMEMBER

- Forces and acceleration are vectors that can be represented by a magnitude (size) and a direction given by an arrow, from M1.
- The *suvat* equations for motion with constant acceleration from M1.
- Drawing force diagrams from M1.

K KEY FACTS

- Newton's second law:
  Resultant force = mass × acceleration or **F** = m**a**.
  For motion in a straight line this is often written as $F = ma$.
- The acceleration is in the same direction as the resultant force.
- The equation obtained is often referred to as the 'equation of motion'.
- The S.I. unit of force is the newton, and for acceleration the S.I. unit is $m\,s^{-2}$.
- A force of 1 newton gives a mass of 1 kg an acceleration of $1\,m\,s^{-2}$.

A ADVICE

Acceleration and force are different quantities so it is helpful to use different types of arrow for these. For example, force: $\longrightarrow$ acceleration: $\twoheadrightarrow$

EXAMPLE 1

A sledge of mass 12 kg is being pulled by a horizontal rope against a resistance of 2 N. The tension in the rope is 5 N. What is the acceleration of the sledge?

SOLUTION

The resultant horizontal force = $(5 - 2)$ and $m = 12$
Using Newton's second law $5 - 2 = 12a$
The acceleration is $3 \div 12 = 0.25\,m\,s^{-2}$.

EXAMPLE 2	A racing driver of mass 70 kg survived after hitting a wall at 48 m s^{-1} and stopping in 0.66 m. What was the average magnitude of the force acting on the driver?

SOLUTION

You are given that $u = 48$, $v = 0$ and $s = 0.66$, so the acceleration can be calculated using

$$v^2 = u^2 + 2as$$
$$0 = 48^2 + 2 \times 0.66 \times a$$
$$-1.32a = 2304$$

So
$$a = -2304 \div 1.32$$
$$= -1745.45...$$

> The driver slowed down so the acceleration was negative.

By Newton's second law, the force acting was
mass $\times$ acceleration $= 70 \times 1745.45...$ N
$$= 122\,181.81...$$ N
$$\text{Force} = 122.2 \text{ kN (1 d.p.)}$$

> This is a massive force, but it is based on a true story.

EXAMPLE 3	A girl of mass 50 kg is going up in a lift. Calculate the force between the girl and the floor of the lift: **i)** when it is accelerating upwards at 0.5 m s^{-2} **ii)** when it is moving upwards at a steady speed **iii)** when it is slowing down at 0.4 m s^{-2}.

SOLUTION

i) The diagram shows the acceleration and forces acting on the girl.
The girl's weight is $50g$ N and the acceleration is
$$a = +0.5 \text{ m s}^{-2}$$
The resultant force upwards is
$$R - 50g \text{ N}.$$
By Newton's second law:
$$R - 50g = 50 \times 0.5$$
So
$$R = 25 + 50 \times 9.8$$
$$= 515$$
The force between the girl and the floor is 515 N.

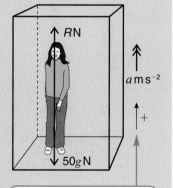

> Notice that upwards is taken as the positive direction.

ii) When the speed is steady, $a = 0$ and the forces on the girl are in equilibrium.
Hence the reaction force = the girl's weight
$$= 50g$$
$$= 490 \text{ N}$$

iii) When the lift is slowing down, $a = -0.4$ so
$$R - 50g = 50 \times (-0.4)$$
$$R = 50 \times 9.8 - 20$$
$$= 470$$
The force between the girl and the floor is 470 N.

EXAMPLE 4

A skydiver of mass 80 kg dives from rest and reaches a speed of 96 m s^{-1} in 20 s.

i) What constant force would produce the same result?

He then spreads himself out to reduce speed and falls a further 220 m before opening his parachute; his speed is then 53 m s^{-1}.

ii) What constant air resistance would give this result?

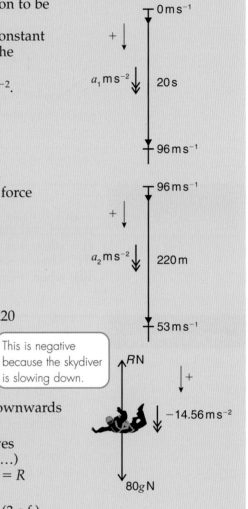

i) Take the downwards direction to be positive, as in the diagram.

As you are asked to find a constant force, you can assume that the acceleration is constant.

Let the acceleration $= a_1 \text{ m s}^{-2}$.

$u = 0$, $v = 96$, $t = 20$, $a_1 = ?$

Use
$$v = u + a_1 t$$
$$96 = 0 + 20a_1$$
$$a_1 = \frac{96}{20} = 4.8$$

The acceleration is 4.8 m s^{-2}.

Now use $\mathbf{F} = m\mathbf{a}$ to find the force
$$F = 80 \times 4.8$$
$$= 384$$

The force would be 384 N.

ii) Now $u = 96$, $v = 53$, $s = 220$,

new acceleration $= a_2 \text{ m s}^{-2}$

Use
$$v^2 = u^2 + 2a_2 s$$
$$53^2 = 96^2 + 2 \times a_2 \times 220$$
$$53^2 - 96^2 = 440a_2$$
$$-6407 = 440a_2$$
$$a_2 = -\frac{6407}{440}$$
$$a_2 = -14.56\ldots$$

> This is negative because the skydiver is slowing down.

The resultant force acting downwards is $80g - R$.

So Newton's second law gives
$$80g - R = 80 \times (-14.56\ldots)$$
$$80 \times 9.8 + 80 \times 14.56\ldots = R$$
$$R = 1948.908\ldots$$

The air resistance is 1.95 kN (3 s.f.).

LINKS

Mechanics   Vectors (M1), Forces and motion in two dimensions (M1), General motion (M1).
Many topics in these units use Newton's second law extensively (M2, M3, M4).

Test Yourself ⊃L

1 In a road safety test, a car containing a dummy of mass 60 kg is made to collide with a wall. Initially the car is moving at $16\,\text{m s}^{-1}$ and it buckles when it hits the wall. What average force acts on the dummy if it moves forwards 0.8 m before stopping?

   A 9600 N   B 9012 N   C 1200 N   D 588 N

2 A parachutist of mass 75 kg is descending with a downwards acceleration of $5.2\,\text{m s}^{-2}$. At this point the upthrust acting on the parachutist is $U\,\text{N}$. Later, the upthrust has doubled. What is his new acceleration?

   A $2.6\,\text{m s}^{-2}$ B $1.67\,\text{m s}^{-2}$ C $0.6\,\text{m s}^{-2}$ D $0\,\text{m s}^{-2}$

3 A block of mass 12 kg is being pushed along a rough horizontal plane by a horizontal force of 24 N. The block starts from rest and when it reaches a speed of $1.5\,\text{m s}^{-1}$ the force is removed. There is a constant frictional resistance to motion of 15 N. The block slows down and comes to rest. For how long from start to finish is the block moving?

   A 1.2 s   B 1.95 s   C 2 s   D 3.2 s

4 You are testing your new bathroom scales in an empty shop lift going up several floors without stopping in between.
   When will the scales show you as heavier than you really are?

   A Never, they will always be correct

   B When the lift starts moving

   C Halfway up

   D When the lift slows down

Exam-Style Question ⊃L

A car of mass 1000 kg is travelling along a straight, horizontal road.

i) Calculate the acceleration of the car when a resultant force of 2000 N acts on it in the direction of its motion.
   How long does it take the car to increase its speed from $5\,\text{m s}^{-1}$ to $12.5\,\text{m s}^{-1}$?

ii) The car has an acceleration of $1.4\,\text{m s}^{-2}$ when there is a driving force of 2000 N. Calculate the resistance to motion of the car.

Connected particles

You often come across moving objects which are connected together, such as a train pulling carriages or freight trucks, or a car towing a trailer or caravan. This topic covers what you need to know in order to apply Newton's second law to the motion of such objects.

- The *suvat* equations for motion with constant acceleration from M1.
- Solving simultaneous equations from C1.
- Drawing force diagrams from M1.
- Newton's second law: resultant force = mass × acceleration, or **F** = m**a**, from M1.

- The acceleration is in the same direction as the resultant force.

- The equation obtained is often referred to as the 'equation of motion'.

- The magnitudes of the velocity and acceleration of two objects connected by an inextensible string or rod are always the same.

- The tension in a string passing over a smooth light pulley is the same on both sides of the pulley.

When two or more objects are connected, there are usually several possible equations of motion you can write down.

You can consider all the particles together as one big mass, or you can treat one or more of them separately as separate masses each with their own forces.

Always remember that, when the connection is rigid (as is the case in the following question), the speed and acceleration of the objects must always be the same because they are attached.

When a pulley is involved, the directions might be different.

EXAMPLE 1

Blocks A of mass 2 kg and B of mass 3 kg are joined together and sliding on smooth ice under the action of a force F N acting on the first block A. The tension in the joining rod is T N and the acceleration is a m s^{-2}. Write down the equations of motion for:
i) the combined system
ii) block A
iii) block B.

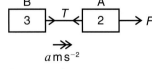

Forces in N

SOLUTION

i) The first diagram shows the combined body as a large block with mass 5 kg. The only force acting is F N. Its equation of motion is:
$$F = 5a \qquad ①$$

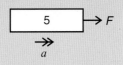

ii) The second diagram shows the block A. It has the forwards force F N and the backwards tension T N acting on it. Its equation of motion is:
$$F - T = 2a \qquad ②$$

iii) The third diagram shows the block B. It has only the forwards tension T N acting on it. Its equation of motion is
$$T = 3a \qquad ③$$

Notice that you can eliminate T from equations ② and ③ by adding them:
$$F - T + T = 2a + 3a$$
Giving $\qquad F = 5a \qquad$ which is equation ①

There are in fact only two equations rather than three which you can use.
Choose the two most appropriate ones. The third gives you no more information, but can be used as a check.

EXAMPLE 2

An engine of mass 80 000 kg is shunting a truck of mass 4000 kg into some sidings. The driving force of the engine is 2500 N and there are resistances of 200 N on each of the engine and the truck. Calculate the force in the coupling between the engine and the truck. Is it in tension or compression?

SOLUTION

The diagram shows the engine pushing the truck towards the right. For the time being, the force in the coupling is shown as a **tension** T newtons ($\rightarrow\!\!\leftarrow$). The acceleration is a m s^{-2}.

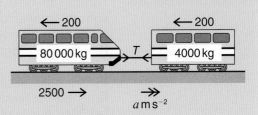

Forces in newtons

Using $\mathbf{F} = m\mathbf{a}$ for each separately gives
Engine: $T + 2500 - 200 = 80\,000a$
$\qquad\qquad T + 2300 = 80\,000a \qquad ①$
Truck: $\qquad -T - 200 = 4000a \qquad ②$

> Notice that the resultant force is taken to be in the same direction as the acceleration.

Eliminate a by multiplying ② by 20
$$-20T - 4000 = 80\,000a$$

> Alternatively, you can add ① and ② to find $a = \frac{1}{40}$ then substitute in ② to find T.

then equating to ①, giving
$$-20T - 4000 = T + 2300$$
$$-4000 - 2300 = 21T$$
So $\quad T = -\frac{6300}{21} = -300$

> If the force in the coupling had been shown as a thrust, it would have turned out to be positive 300 N.

The **tension** is negative 300 newtons, indicating that the force in the coupling is in fact a **thrust** or **compression** ($\leftarrow\!\!\rightarrow$) of 300 N: forwards on the truck and backwards on the engine.

EXAMPLE 3

A boat of mass 1500 kg is pulling a waterskier of mass 65 kg. The driving force of the boat's engine is 8000 N. There are resistances of 1000 N on the boat and 100 N on the skier.
Calculate the acceleration and the tension in the tow rope pulling the skier.

SOLUTION

The diagram shows the horizontal forces acting on the boat and skier.
You can calculate the acceleration by considering them both together.

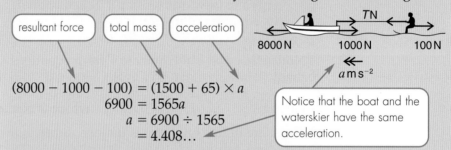

(resultant force) (total mass) (acceleration)

$$(8000 - 1000 - 100) = (1500 + 65) \times a$$
$$6900 = 1565a$$
$$a = 6900 \div 1565$$
$$= 4.408\ldots$$

Notice that the boat and the waterskier have the same acceleration.

To calculate the tension, you need to consider the motion of the boat or the skier alone.
For the waterskier:

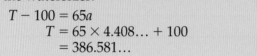

$$T - 100 = 65a$$
$$T = 65 \times 4.408\ldots + 100$$
$$= 386.581\ldots$$

mass = 65 kg

The acceleration is 4.41 m s^{-2} and the tension in the rope is 387 N (both to 3 s.f.).

EXAMPLE 4

Particles of mass 0.5 kg (A) and 0.3 kg (B) are attached to the ends of a light string which hangs vertically over a smooth light pulley. The system is released from rest.
i) Draw a diagram to show the forces and acceleration of the particles.
ii) Find the acceleration of the system.
iii) Find the tension in the string.
iv) Find the velocities of A and B after 2 seconds.

SOLUTION

i) The forces acting are the weight of each particle and the tension, T, in the string. The particle A is heavier so it will move downwards and B will move upwards. The acceleration is $a\,\mathrm{m\,s^{-2}}$.
The diagram shows the forces and the accelerations of A and B.

ii) Write the equations of motion of A and B, each in the direction of its motion.
For A ($\downarrow$): $\qquad 0.5g - T = 0.5a \qquad$ ①
For B ($\uparrow$): $\qquad T - 0.3g = 0.3a \qquad$ ②
When these equations are added, the tension T is eliminated so:
$$0.5g - 0.3g = 0.5a + 0.3a$$
$$0.2g = 0.8a$$
The acceleration is $0.2g \div 0.8 = 2.45\,\mathrm{m\,s^{-2}}$.

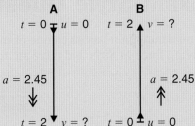

iii) Substitute this in ② to calculate T:
$$T - 0.3g = 0.3 \times 2.45$$
$$T = 0.735 + 0.3 \times 9.8$$
$$= 3.675$$
The tension is $3.68\,\mathrm{N}$ (3 s.f.).

iv) Take the direction of motion to be positive.
For each particle, $u = 0$, $a = 2.45$, $t = 2$.
To calculate v after 2 seconds use
$$v = u + at$$
$$v = 0 + 2.45 \times 2$$
A has downwards velocity $4.9\,\mathrm{m\,s^{-1}}$.
B is moving upwards at $4.9\,\mathrm{m\,s^{-1}}$.

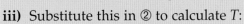

LINKS

Mechanics   Vectors (M1), Forces and motion in two dimensions (M1), General motion (M1).

Test Yourself

Use the following information for **questions 1 and 2**.

A car of mass 800 kg is pulling a trailer of mass 600 kg along a straight level road. There is a resistance of 90 N on the car and 200 N on the trailer and they are slowing down at a rate of $0.8\,\mathrm{m\,s^{-2}}$.

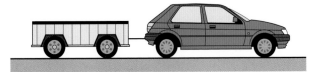

1 Calculate the braking force required.

   A 550 N   B 830 N   C 1120 N   D 1410 N

2 By considering the motion of the trailer, calculate the force in the tow bar.

   A Thrust of 680 N   B Thrust of 280 N   C Tension of 200 N   D Tension of 280 N

Use the following information for **questions 3 and 4**.

A block of mass 3 kg is held on a rough table. A light inextensible string attached to the block passes over a smooth pulley and a sphere of mass 2 kg hangs from the other end. The block is then released and allowed to slide on the table against a friction force of 10 N.
The tension in the string is T N and the acceleration of the system is a m s^{-2}.

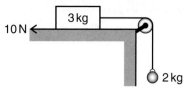

3 Draw a diagram for yourself showing the forces acting on the block and the sphere and their accelerations. Use your diagram to write down their equations of motion.
Three of the following equations are incorrect and one is correct. Which one is correct?

     A $T = 2a$ **B** $T - 10 - 3g = 3a$

     C $2g - T = 2ga$ **D** $T - 10 = 3a$

4 Which of the following shows the acceleration of the block?

     A 4.8 m s^{-2} **B** 1.92 m s^{-2} **C** 9.6 m s^{-2} **D** 29.6 m s^{-2}

Exam-Style Question 🔲

A miniature train has an engine of mass 30 kg and 4 trucks each of mass 2.5 kg. The engine produces a driving force of 80 N and there are resistances of 48 N on the engine and 3 N on each truck.

Calculate:
i)   the total resistance and the acceleration of the train
ii)   the tension in the coupling between the last two trucks
iii) the tension in the coupling between the engine and the first truck.

Vectors

5

Vector notation

A ABOUT THIS TOPIC

An understanding of vectors is essential to the study of mechanics. A vector is a way of conveying information about the size (magnitude) and direction of a quantity. This section is about the notations used to describe vectors.

R REMEMBER

- Pythagoras' theorem from GCSE and C1.
- Basic trigonometry including the sine and cosine rules from Higher Tier GCSE.

K KEY FACTS

- A vector has magnitude and direction and can be represented by a straight line segment of an appropriate length and direction.

  For example, $\overrightarrow{PQ}$

  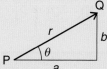

  The vector may also be written in component form as $\overrightarrow{PQ} = a\mathbf{i} + b\mathbf{j}$ or as $\overrightarrow{PQ} = \begin{pmatrix} a \\ b \end{pmatrix}$ where $\mathbf{i}$ and $\mathbf{j}$ are unit vectors in the x and y directions.
  (In 3-D, $\mathbf{k}$ is the unit vector in the z direction.)

- The vector $\mathbf{r} = a\mathbf{i} + b\mathbf{j}$ has a magnitude $\sqrt{a^2 + b^2}$ and direction θ given by $\tan\theta = \dfrac{b}{a}$.
  (The magnitude of vector $\mathbf{r} = a\mathbf{i} + b\mathbf{j} + c\mathbf{k}$ is given by $\sqrt{a^2 + b^2 + c^2}$.)

- A position vector starts at the origin. For example, $\overrightarrow{OP}$ is a position vector.

  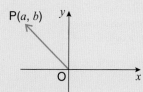

- Vectors are often written as single letters. They may be underlined or in bold type, that is $\underset{\sim}{m}$ or $\mathbf{m}$.
- The vector $\overrightarrow{MN}$ in the diagram (from M to N) is given by $\overrightarrow{MN} = \mathbf{n} - \mathbf{m}$.

  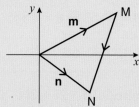

- $\mathbf{a}$ and $3\mathbf{a}$ are 'like' parallel vectors; $\mathbf{b}$ and $-2\mathbf{b}$ are 'unlike' parallel vectors (i.e. in the same direction but in the opposite sense to each other).
- Vectors in component form are added term by term, i.e. $\begin{pmatrix} a \\ b \end{pmatrix} + \begin{pmatrix} c \\ d \end{pmatrix} = \begin{pmatrix} a + c \\ b + d \end{pmatrix}$.
- Vectors represented as line segments can be added 'nose to tail' so that the arrows follow round in order. The *resultant* is the vector that goes from the start of the first vector to the end of the last one. If the vectors form a closed polygon then the vector sum is zero.

5 Vectors

EXAMPLE 1

Write the vectors shown in the figure in column vector form.

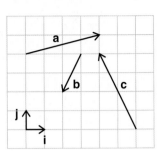

SOLUTION

$$\mathbf{a} = \begin{pmatrix} 4 \\ 1 \end{pmatrix}, \mathbf{b} = \begin{pmatrix} -1 \\ -2 \end{pmatrix}, \mathbf{c} = \begin{pmatrix} -2 \\ 4 \end{pmatrix}$$

A ADVICE

Be careful with signs.
Take notice of the way the arrow is pointing on the vector.

EXAMPLE 2

Find the magnitude and the direction of the following vectors.
i) $2\mathbf{i} - 2\mathbf{j}$ **ii)** $-2\mathbf{i} + 2\mathbf{j}$

SOLUTION

i) The magnitude of $2\mathbf{i} - 2\mathbf{j}$ is given by $\sqrt{2^2 + (-2)^2} = 2\sqrt{2}$ and the direction by angle θ so that $\tan \theta = \frac{-2}{2} = -1$, that is $\theta = 315°$ (or $-45°$).

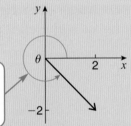

The angle θ is measured from the positive x axis and in the anticlockwise direction.

A ADVICE

$\tan \theta = -1$ has two solutions between $0°$ and $360°$: $\theta = 315°$ or $\theta = 135°$. By drawing a diagram you can see clearly that the solution you need in this case is in the fourth quadrant.

ii) The magnitude of $-2\mathbf{i} + 2\mathbf{j}$ is also $2\sqrt{2}$ and the direction θ also has $\tan \theta = -1$ but in this case the solution you want is $\theta = 135°$.

A ADVICE

Always draw a diagram to show the examiner exactly which angle you mean.

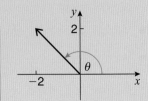

Vectors

EXAMPLE 3

$\mathbf{a} = \begin{pmatrix} 2 \\ 4 \end{pmatrix}$, $\mathbf{b} = \begin{pmatrix} 3 \\ -2 \end{pmatrix}$ and $\mathbf{c} = \begin{pmatrix} 5 \\ -2 \end{pmatrix}$.

Find the resultant vectors **i)** $\mathbf{a} + \mathbf{b}$ **ii)** $3\mathbf{a} + \mathbf{b} - 2\mathbf{c}$.

SOLUTION

i) $\mathbf{a} + \mathbf{b} = \begin{pmatrix} 2 \\ 4 \end{pmatrix} + \begin{pmatrix} 3 \\ -2 \end{pmatrix} = \begin{pmatrix} 5 \\ 2 \end{pmatrix}$

ii) $3\mathbf{a} + \mathbf{b} - 2\mathbf{c} = 3\begin{pmatrix} 2 \\ 4 \end{pmatrix} + \begin{pmatrix} 3 \\ -2 \end{pmatrix} - 2\begin{pmatrix} 5 \\ -2 \end{pmatrix}$

$= \begin{pmatrix} 6 \\ 12 \end{pmatrix} + \begin{pmatrix} 3 \\ -2 \end{pmatrix} - \begin{pmatrix} 10 \\ -4 \end{pmatrix}$

$= \begin{pmatrix} -1 \\ 14 \end{pmatrix}$

R RULE

A resultant is obtained when two or more vectors are added together. The algebraic solution to part i) is given above. On a diagram this could be represented by adding **a** to **b** 'nose to tail', so that the resultant, $\mathbf{a} + \mathbf{b}$, joins the tail of **a** to the nose of **b**.

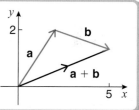

EXAMPLE 4

A, B and C are the points (2, 3), (4, −1) and (−3, −2) respectively.
i) Write down the position vectors of these points in component form.
ii) Find the displacements $\overrightarrow{AB}$, $\overrightarrow{BC}$ and $\overrightarrow{CA}$.
iii) Show that $\overrightarrow{AB} + \overrightarrow{BC} + \overrightarrow{CA} = 0$ and interpret this result.

SOLUTION

i) Let $\overrightarrow{OA} = \mathbf{a} = \begin{pmatrix} 2 \\ 3 \end{pmatrix}$, $\overrightarrow{OB} = \mathbf{b} = \begin{pmatrix} 4 \\ -1 \end{pmatrix}$ and $\overrightarrow{OC} = \mathbf{c} = \begin{pmatrix} -3 \\ -2 \end{pmatrix}$.

ii) $\overrightarrow{AB} = \mathbf{b} - \mathbf{a} = \begin{pmatrix} 4 \\ -1 \end{pmatrix} - \begin{pmatrix} 2 \\ 3 \end{pmatrix} = \begin{pmatrix} 2 \\ -4 \end{pmatrix}$

$\overrightarrow{BC} = \mathbf{c} - \mathbf{b} = \begin{pmatrix} -3 \\ -2 \end{pmatrix} - \begin{pmatrix} 4 \\ -1 \end{pmatrix} = \begin{pmatrix} -7 \\ -1 \end{pmatrix}$

$\overrightarrow{CA} = \mathbf{a} - \mathbf{c} = \begin{pmatrix} 2 \\ 3 \end{pmatrix} - \begin{pmatrix} -3 \\ -2 \end{pmatrix} = \begin{pmatrix} 5 \\ 5 \end{pmatrix}$

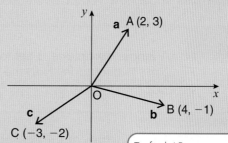

To find AB you need to think about this as a journey from A to O and then from O to B as this takes you along vectors that you know. From A to O is −**a** because this is in the opposite direction to OA. O to B is **b**. So moving from A to B is $\overrightarrow{AB}$ which is $-\mathbf{a} + \mathbf{b} = \mathbf{b} - \mathbf{a}$.

iii) $\overrightarrow{AB} + \overrightarrow{BC} + \overrightarrow{CA} = 2\mathbf{i} - 4\mathbf{j} - 7\mathbf{i} - \mathbf{j} + 5\mathbf{i} + 5\mathbf{j} = 0$
$\overrightarrow{AB} + \overrightarrow{BC} + \overrightarrow{CA}$ form a closed triangle when added 'nose to tail'.

EXAMPLE 5

i) Find a unit vector in the direction $\begin{pmatrix} 2 \\ -4 \end{pmatrix}$.

ii) Hence find a force **F** with magnitude $3\sqrt{5}\,\text{N}$ in the direction $\begin{pmatrix} 2 \\ -4 \end{pmatrix}$.

SOLUTION

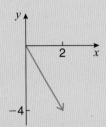

i) Using Pythagoras' theorem (from this figure), the magnitude (or length) of $\begin{pmatrix} 2 \\ -4 \end{pmatrix}$ is given by $\sqrt{2^2 + (-4)^2} = \sqrt{20} = 2\sqrt{5}$.

So a unit vector in this direction is $\dfrac{1}{2\sqrt{5}}\begin{pmatrix} 2 \\ -4 \end{pmatrix} = \begin{pmatrix} \frac{2}{2\sqrt{5}} \\ \frac{-4}{2\sqrt{5}} \end{pmatrix} = \begin{pmatrix} \frac{1}{\sqrt{5}} \\ \frac{-2}{\sqrt{5}} \end{pmatrix}$

> **F** is $3\sqrt{5}$ times as big as the unit vector.

ii) $\mathbf{F} = 3\sqrt{5} \times \begin{pmatrix} \frac{1}{\sqrt{5}} \\ \frac{-2}{\sqrt{5}} \end{pmatrix} = \begin{pmatrix} 3 \\ -6 \end{pmatrix}$

A ADVICE

Although many questions are set out in $a\mathbf{i} + b\mathbf{j}$ component form you may find it easier to work in column vector notation, that is $\begin{pmatrix} a \\ b \end{pmatrix}$. This can make it easier to spot and avoid errors, particularly in problems in 3-D.

The next two examples show how vector addition can be used in a physical situation.

EXAMPLE 6

A model aeroplane is set to fly at $12\,\text{m s}^{-1}$ due west. A wind blows at $5\,\text{m s}^{-1}$ due north. Find the resultant velocity of the aeroplane.

SOLUTION

The velocities of the aeroplane and the wind will add together to give the resultant velocity of the plane. First draw a diagram showing this, remembering to add nose to tail.

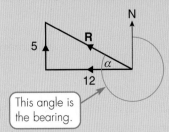

> This angle is the bearing.

By Pythagoras' theorem,
$$R = \sqrt{5^2 + 12^2} = \sqrt{169} = 13$$
$$\tan \alpha = \tfrac{5}{12}$$
$$\therefore \quad \alpha = 22.619\ldots°$$

The resultant velocity of the aeroplane is $13\,\text{m s}^{-1}$ on a bearing of $293°$ (3 s.f.).

EXAMPLE 7

A boy wishes to row to a small island which is due west of his current position. He knows that he can row at 10 km h⁻¹ in still water and that a current of 3 km h⁻¹ flows in a direction 150°. What course should he steer to reach the island?

SOLUTION

The boy's resultant velocity is in the direction due west. It is the sum of his velocity through the water (10 km h⁻¹ in an unknown direction) and the current (3 km h⁻¹ at 150°). This information is shown on the diagram.

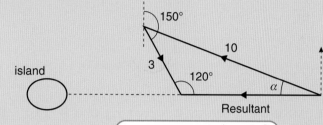

island

Resultant

Using the sine rule ← [In triangle ABC, $\frac{\sin A}{a} = \frac{\sin B}{b}$]

$$\frac{\sin 120°}{10} = \frac{\sin \alpha}{3} \quad \therefore \alpha = 15.05...°$$

The course he needs to steer has a bearing $(270 + 15.05...)$
$= 285°$ (3 s.f.).

LINKS

Pure Mathematics   Vectors and co-ordinate geometry (C4, FP1, FP3).
Mechanics   Vectors of physical quantities (M1, M2, M3, M4).

Test Yourself ▷L

1 A child runs from the front to the back of a bus. The bus is travelling due south at 25 m s⁻¹. The child is running at 0.5 m s⁻¹. What is the resultant velocity of the child?

A 24.5 m s⁻¹ due S
B 24.5 m s⁻¹ due N
C 25.5 m s⁻¹ due N
D 25.5 m s⁻¹ due S

2 The vector $\mathbf{b} = -8\mathbf{i} + 15\mathbf{j}$. Find its magnitude and direction.

A 17 units and 61.9° to the positive x axis

B 17 units and 118.1° to the positive x axis

C 12.7 units and 118.1° to the positive x axis

D 17 units and −61.9° to the positive x axis

3 You are given that $\mathbf{a} = 2\mathbf{i} - 4\mathbf{j} + 3\mathbf{k}$, $\mathbf{b} = -3\mathbf{i} + \mathbf{k}$ and $\mathbf{c} = 2\mathbf{j} - 3\mathbf{k}$. Find the vector $2\mathbf{a} - \mathbf{b} - \mathbf{c}$.

A $7\mathbf{i} - 11\mathbf{j} + 9\mathbf{k}$
B $7\mathbf{i} - 10\mathbf{j} + 8\mathbf{k}$
C $7\mathbf{i} - 10\mathbf{j} + 2\mathbf{k}$
D $\mathbf{i} - 10\mathbf{j} + 8\mathbf{k}$

4 Find a vector with magnitude 50 in the direction $\begin{pmatrix} -7 \\ 24 \end{pmatrix}$.

A $\begin{pmatrix} -14 \\ 48 \end{pmatrix}$

B $\begin{pmatrix} -350 \\ 1200 \end{pmatrix}$

C $\begin{pmatrix} \frac{-7}{50} \\ \frac{12}{25} \end{pmatrix}$

D $\begin{pmatrix} \frac{-7}{25} \\ \frac{24}{25} \end{pmatrix}$

5 Vectors **a** and **b** are given by $\mathbf{a} = -3\mathbf{i} + \mathbf{j}$ and $\mathbf{b} = \mathbf{i} - 2\mathbf{j}$. Find the magnitude and direction of the resultant of **a** and **b**.

A 5 units in direction 323.1° to the positive x axis

B $\sqrt{5}$ units in direction 26.6° to the positive x axis

C $\sqrt{5}$ units in direction 206.6° to the positive x axis

D 5 units in direction 143.1° to the positive x axis

6 A helicopter with a speed in still air of 60 m.p.h. needs to fly to a spot Q 80 miles away on a bearing of 320° from its current position P. The wind is blowing at 10 m.p.h. from the west. What course should the pilot steer?

A 313°   B 140°   C 327°   D 047°

Exam-Style Question 〗L

The position vectors for points P and Q are $\mathbf{p} = -4\mathbf{i} + 3\mathbf{j}$ and $\mathbf{q} = 5\mathbf{i}$ respectively.

i)   Find the distances from O to P and from O to Q. What can you conclude about triangle OPQ? Find also the length PQ.

ii) M is the mid-point of PQ. Find the magnitude and direction of $\overrightarrow{OM}$.

iii) Show that $\overrightarrow{OM}$ is perpendicular to $\overrightarrow{PQ}$.

iv) Find the area of triangle OPQ.

Resolution

A ABOUT THIS TOPIC

As you have already seen in the previous section, vectors can be added together to produce a single resultant vector. Therefore, there seems no reason why a single vector cannot be replaced by two (or even more) vectors. Splitting a single vector into two components is a process called *resolving* and is a skill that is essential to acquire when studying Mechanics.

R REMEMBER

- Pythagoras' theorem from GCSE and C1.
- Basic trigonometry from GCSE.

K KEY FACTS

- A vector can be resolved into two component vectors. These are usually two vectors at right angles to each other. (This makes it easier to use Pythagoras' theorem and trigonometry.)

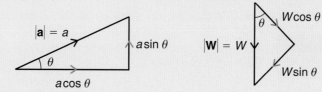 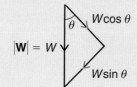

- If the vector is resolved in **i** and **j** directions then the vector can be written in component form as $\mathbf{a} = a \cos \theta \mathbf{i} + a \sin \theta \mathbf{j}$

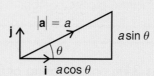

- When resolving it is important to show the directions in which the vector is to be resolved clearly. Always draw a diagram.

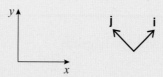

- It is important to make the positive direction clear.

- Resolving can be used to add vectors together. To do this each vector has to be resolved into two components in agreed directions, for example **i** and **j** (or x and y).

- If the sum of the **i** components is written as R_1 and that of the **j** components written as R_2, then the resultant vector has a magnitude of $\sqrt{R_1^2 + R_2^2}$ and is in a direction θ where $\tan \theta = \dfrac{R_2}{R_1}$.

  A diagram needs to be drawn to make it very clear which angle is being taken as θ.

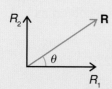 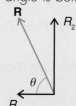

EXAMPLE 1

Write down the following vectors in component form.

i)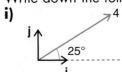

ii)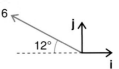

SOLUTION

i)

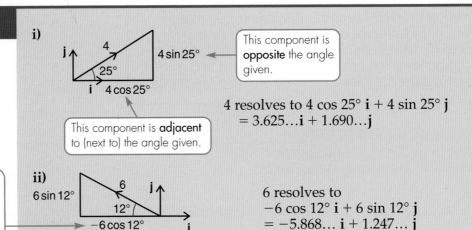

This component is **opposite** the angle given.

This component is **adjacent** to (next to) the angle given.

4 resolves to $4 \cos 25° \, \mathbf{i} + 4 \sin 25° \, \mathbf{j}$
$= 3.625...\mathbf{i} + 1.690...\mathbf{j}$

ii)

You need a negative sign here because the component is in the negative direction of **i**.

6 resolves to
$-6 \cos 12° \, \mathbf{i} + 6 \sin 12° \, \mathbf{j}$
$= -5.868... \, \mathbf{i} + 1.247... \, \mathbf{j}$

A ADVICE

Answers written in the form 3.625... imply that they have not been rounded. If you round values before your final answer, this can lead to inaccurate answers. Always keep as many figures as you can in your calculator while working through a calculation; round off at the end to a suitable number of decimal places or significant figures.

EXAMPLE 2

A man walks 3 km on a bearing of 060° then 2 km due north. Find, in component form, his resultant displacement from his starting point in directions **i** and **j** where **i** is a unit vector due east and **j** is a unit vector due north.

SOLUTION

 Remember bearings are measured clockwise from North.

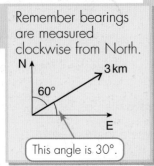

This angle is 30°.

Start by drawing a diagram.

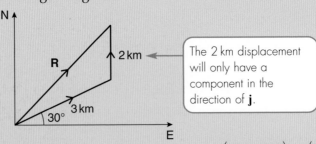

The 2 km displacement will only have a component in the direction of **j**.

The 3 km displacement can be resolved into $\begin{pmatrix} 3 \cos 30° \\ 3 \sin 30° \end{pmatrix} = \begin{pmatrix} 2.598... \\ 1.5 \end{pmatrix}$.

The 2 km displacement can be resolved as $\begin{pmatrix} 0 \\ 2 \end{pmatrix}$.

Adding these together gives $\begin{pmatrix} 0 \\ 2 \end{pmatrix} + \begin{pmatrix} 2.598... \\ 1.5 \end{pmatrix} = \begin{pmatrix} 2.60 \\ 3.50 \end{pmatrix}$ to 2 d.p.

which is the same as $2.60\mathbf{i} + 3.50\mathbf{j}$.

EXAMPLE 3

Vectors of magnitudes 5, 9, and 3 act on a body. They act on bearings of 060°, 300° and 180° respectively.
i) Find, in component form, the resultant, **R**, of the three vectors.
ii) Draw a diagram showing the resultant.
iii) Work out the magnitude and direction of the resultant.

SOLUTION

i)

> ### A ADVICE
>
> Start by drawing sketches of the three vectors. This will help you get the directions right.
>
>

Resolve each vector in turn into $a\mathbf{i} + b\mathbf{j}$ form.
5 resolves to $\quad 5\sin 60°\,\mathbf{i} + 5\cos 60°\,\mathbf{j} = \quad 4.330...\mathbf{i} + 2.5\mathbf{j}$
9 resolves to $\quad -9\sin 60°\,\mathbf{i} + 9\cos 60°\,\mathbf{j} = -7.794...\mathbf{i} + 4.5\mathbf{j}$
3 resolves to $\qquad\qquad\qquad\qquad\qquad = \qquad\qquad\quad -3.0\mathbf{j}$
Add like components together $\qquad\qquad = -3.464...\mathbf{i} + 4.0\mathbf{j}$

Resultant $\mathbf{R} = -3.46\mathbf{i} + 4\mathbf{j}$ (2 d.p.)

ii)

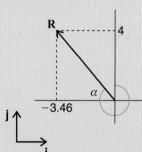

iii) Use Pythagoras to find the magnitude of **R**.
$|\mathbf{R}| = \sqrt{(-3.464...)^2 + 4^2} = \sqrt{28.000...}$
$\qquad = 5.29$ (2 d.p.)
From the diagram
$\tan \alpha = \frac{4}{3.46}$
Therefore $\alpha = 49.10...°$

Because a diagram has been drawn, you can see that the bearing for the resultant must be given by $(270 + 49.10...) = 319°$ (nearest degree).

Notice that the resultant **R** could have been found by adding the vectors nose to tail.

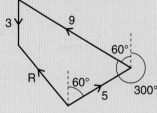

> ### A ADVICE
>
> Always draw a diagram (even when the question doesn't ask you to) showing the direction of the resultant. It helps you avoid problems with signs when using trigonometry and also makes it very clear to anyone reading the solution how the bearing has been derived.

 LINKS

Pure Mathematics   Vectors, co-ordinate geometry and matrices (C4, FP1, FP3).
Mechanics   Vectors of physical quantities (M2, M3, M4).

Test Yourself **⊃L**

1 Find, in terms of **i** and **j**, the resultant of the forces shown in the diagram.

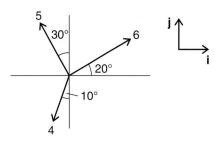

A $-1.14\mathbf{i} + 6.03\mathbf{j}$　　**B** $2.44\mathbf{i} + 2.44\mathbf{j}$　　**C** $-2.63\mathbf{i} - 3.86\mathbf{j}$　　**D** $9.56\mathbf{i} + 9.61\mathbf{j}$

2 A man walks 100 m north then 250 m south-east. By writing each displacement as a column vector in directions east and north, find his resultant displacement from his starting point, giving your answers correct to the nearest whole number.

A $\begin{pmatrix} 277 \\ -177 \end{pmatrix}$　　　　**B** $\begin{pmatrix} 177 \\ 277 \end{pmatrix}$　　　　**C** $\begin{pmatrix} 177 \\ -77 \end{pmatrix}$　　　　**D** $\begin{pmatrix} -177 \\ 77 \end{pmatrix}$

3 Find the magnitude of the resultant of the vectors shown in the diagram.

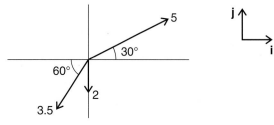

A 0.79 units　　　　**B** 3.61 units　　　　**C** 2.97 units　　　　**D** 0.51 units

4 The diagram shows a block on a slope. Three of the following statements are false and one is true. Which one is true?

A The vertical component of T is $T \sin \beta$.

B The component of F parallel to the slope is $F \cos \alpha$.

C The component of mg parallel to the slope is $mg \sin \alpha$ down the slope.

D The component of mg perpendicular to the slope is $mg \sin \alpha$.

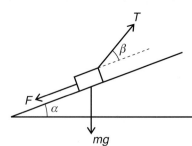

Exam-Style Question ⊃L

The diagram shows four forces acting at a point.

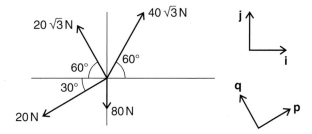

i) Resolve the forces in the diagram in the directions **p** and **q**.

ii) Hence show that the forces are in equilibrium.

iii) Show that if you resolve in the directions **i** and **j** the forces are still in equilibrium.

iv) Describe a physical situation that may give rise to these forces.

Projectiles

6

Projectiles in flight

A ABOUT THIS TOPIC

This section deals with the basic results for the motion of a projectile, which is moving in two dimensions under the influence of only one force, the force of gravity. The projectile is considered as a particle, it is not powered and air resistance has no effect on its motion. More complicated projectile questions will be considered in the next section.

R REMEMBER

- The constant acceleration (*suvat*) equations from M1.
- The acceleration due to gravity, g, is vertically downwards and is usually taken to be 9.8 m s^{-2} (or sometimes 10 m s^{-2}), from M1.
- Resolving vectors from M1 and the previous chapter.

K KEY FACTS

- Projectile motion is usually considered in terms of horizontal and vertical components.

  When the initial position is at O

  Angle of projection $= \alpha$

  Initial velocity, $\mathbf{u} = \begin{pmatrix} u \cos \alpha \\ u \sin \alpha \end{pmatrix}$

  Acceleration, $\mathbf{a} = \begin{pmatrix} 0 \\ -g \end{pmatrix}$

  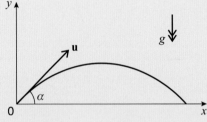

- At time t, velocity, $\mathbf{v} = \mathbf{u} + \mathbf{a}t$ $\qquad \begin{pmatrix} v_x \\ v_y \end{pmatrix} = \begin{pmatrix} u \cos \alpha \\ u \sin \alpha \end{pmatrix} + \begin{pmatrix} 0 \\ -g \end{pmatrix}t$

  Horizontal velocity $\qquad v_x = u \cos \alpha$
  Vertical velocity $\qquad v_y = u \sin \alpha - gt$

- At time t, displacement, $\mathbf{r} = \mathbf{u}t + \frac{1}{2}\mathbf{a}t^2$ $\qquad \begin{pmatrix} x \\ y \end{pmatrix} = \begin{pmatrix} u \cos \alpha \\ u \sin \alpha \end{pmatrix}t + \frac{1}{2}\begin{pmatrix} 0 \\ -g \end{pmatrix}t^2$

  Horizontal displacement $\qquad x = ut \cos \alpha$
  Vertical displacement $\qquad y = ut \sin \alpha - \frac{1}{2}gt^2$

- At the maximum height, the vertical velocity $v_y = 0$.

- When the projectile lands, the vertical displacement (i.e. the height) $y = 0$.

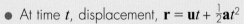

The examples in this section cover different aspects of the flight of a projectile which is launched from a point on level ground with initial velocity 30 m s^{-1} at an angle of $42°$ to the horizontal. The point of projection is taken to be the origin, with the x axis horizontal and the y axis vertical. The value of g is taken to be 9.8 m s^{-2}.

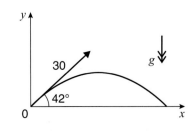

EXAMPLE 1

i) What are the initial values of the horizontal and vertical components of the velocity?

ii) Write down the equations for the velocity and position after t seconds **a)** in component form and **b)** in vector form.

SOLUTION

i) Resolving in the horizontal and vertical directions you get $u_x = 30 \cos 42° = 22.294... = 22.3$ (3 s.f.) and $u_y = 30 \sin 42° = 20.073... = 20.1$ (3 s.f.)

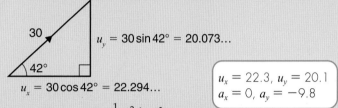

$u_y = 30 \sin 42° = 20.073...$

$u_x = 30 \cos 42° = 22.294...$

$u_x = 22.3, u_y = 20.1$
$a_x = 0, a_y = -9.8$

ii) **a)** Using $v = u + at$, $s = ut + \frac{1}{2}at^2$ in the horizontal and vertical directions, and using rounded values for u_x and u_y as a final answer is being given

	Velocity	Position
Horizontal	$v_x = 22.3$	$x = 22.3t$
Vertical	$v_y = 20.1 - 9.8t$	$y = 20.1t - 4.9t^2$

b) Expressing these in vector form, you get

$$\binom{v_x}{v_y} = \binom{22.3}{20.1} + \binom{0}{-9.8}t \quad \text{and} \quad \binom{x}{y} = \binom{22.3}{20.1}t + \frac{1}{2}\binom{0}{-9.8}t^2$$

EXAMPLE 2

i) What is the time taken for the projectile to reach its highest point?

ii) What is the maximum height?

SOLUTION

i) When the projectile is at its maximum height, H, the **vertical** component of the velocity is zero (though it still has a horizontal component of $22.3 \, \text{m s}^{-1}$).

So $v_y = 0$

$\Rightarrow 20.073... - 9.8t = 0$

$\Rightarrow t = \frac{20.073...}{9.8} = 2.048...$

$v_y = 0$

H

It takes $2.05 \, \text{s}$ (3 s.f.) for the projectile to reach its highest point.

ii) To find the maximum height, H, you need to find y when $t = 2.05$.

So the maximum height

$H = 20.073... \times 2.048... - 4.9(2.048...)^2$

$= 20.559...$

$= 20.6 \, \text{m}$ (3 s.f.).

EXAMPLE 3
i) What is the time of flight of the projectile?
ii) What is the horizontal range?

SOLUTION

The range, R, is the horizontal distance the projectile travels before landing, so R is the value of x when $y = 0$.

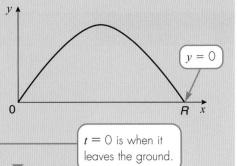

$y = 0$

i) When $y = 0$,
$$(20.073...t - 4.9t^2) = 0$$
$$\Rightarrow \quad t(20.073... - 4.9t) = 0$$
$$\Rightarrow \quad\quad\quad\quad t = 0$$

$t = 0$ is when it leaves the ground.

or $\quad \dfrac{20.073...}{4.9} = 4.096...$

So the time of flight is 4.10 s (3 s.f.).

$t = 4.096...$ is when it lands again.

ii) To find R, substitute $t = 4.096...$ in the equation for x, so $R = 22.294... \times 4.096... = 91.33... = 91.3$ m (3 s.f.) which is the horizontal range.

EXAMPLE 4
Show that the equation of the path of the projectile is $y = 0.900x - 0.00986x^2$.

SOLUTION

It is a parabola.

The path of the projectile is called its *trajectory*.
You know the expressions for x and y in terms of t. They are
$$x = (22.294...)t \quad \text{①} \quad \text{and} \quad y = (20.073...)t - 4.9t^2 \quad \text{②}$$
If you eliminate t, you get an equation relating x and y, which will be the equation of the parabola.

From ① $t = \dfrac{x}{22.294...}$

Substituting for t in ② gives $y = 20.073... \times \left(\dfrac{x}{22.294...}\right) - 4.9\left(\dfrac{x}{22.294...}\right)^2$

This simplifies to give $y = 0.900x - 0.00986x^2$, the equation of the trajectory (coefficients to 3 s.f.).

A | ADVICE

When solving a question on projectiles it is a good idea to start by drawing a diagram, marking on it the information which you are given and then finding the equations for v_x, v_y, x and y.
Most questions, like these examples, can then be solved directly by careful use of the diagram and equations.

LINKS

Mechanics   Resisted motion (M4 and DE), Variable mass (M4 and DE).

Test Yourself ▶L

In these questions take the upward direction as positive and use 9.8 m s^{-2} for g. All the projectiles start at the origin.

1 A particle is projected with a velocity of 30 m s^{-1} at an angle of $36.9°$ to the horizontal. What are the x and y co-ordinates of the position of the particle after time t seconds?

A $x = 24.0t$; $y = 18.0t + 4.9t^2$ B $x = 18.0t$; $y = 24.0t - 4.9t^2$

C $x = 24.0t$; $y = 18.0t - 4.9t^2$ D $x = 24.0$; $y = 18.0 - 9.8t$

2 A ball is kicked with a velocity of 14.7 m s^{-1} at an angle of $30°$ to the horizontal. Find the time taken to reach its highest point and its maximum height.

A 1.50 s; 2.76 m B 0.75 s; 2.76 m C 0.75 s; 9.53 m D 1.50 s; 1.91 m

3 Find the horizontal range and time of flight of a particle that has been projected with a velocity of 21 m s^{-1} at an angle of $60°$.

A 16.9 m; 1.86 s B 39.0 m; 1.86 s C 0 m; 3.71 s D 39.0 m; 3.71 s

4 What is the position, expressed in vector form, after time t seconds, of a projectile with an initial velocity (in m s^{-1}) of $\begin{pmatrix} 12 \\ 5 \end{pmatrix}$?

A $\begin{pmatrix} x \\ y \end{pmatrix} = \begin{pmatrix} 12 \\ 5 \end{pmatrix} + \begin{pmatrix} 0 \\ -9.8 \end{pmatrix}t$ B $\begin{pmatrix} x \\ y \end{pmatrix} = \begin{pmatrix} 12 \\ 5 \end{pmatrix}t + \frac{1}{2}\begin{pmatrix} 0 \\ -9.8 \end{pmatrix}t^2$

C $\begin{pmatrix} x \\ y \end{pmatrix} = \begin{pmatrix} 12 \\ 5 \end{pmatrix}t + \frac{1}{2}\begin{pmatrix} 0 \\ 9.8 \end{pmatrix}t^2$ D $\begin{pmatrix} x \\ y \end{pmatrix} = \begin{pmatrix} 5 \\ 12 \end{pmatrix}t + \frac{1}{2}\begin{pmatrix} -9.8 \\ 0 \end{pmatrix}t^2$

Exam-Style Question ▶L

A cricket ball is hit from ground level with a velocity of 24.5 m s^{-1} at an angle θ to the horizontal where $\cos\theta = 0.8$ and $\sin\theta = 0.6$.

i) Show that, after t seconds, the position of the ball is given by

$\quad x = 19.6t$, $y = 14.7t - 4.9t^2$.

ii) Find the greatest height reached by the ball.

iii) Find the distance travelled before the ball bounces for the first time.

iv) Show that the equation of the trajectory of the ball is

$\quad y = \frac{3}{4}x - \frac{5}{392}x^2$.

Further projectiles

A ABOUT THIS TOPIC

This section develops the ideas introduced in the last section and applies them to more complex situations. The modelling assumptions remain the same but the point of projection is not necessarily the origin.

R REMEMBER

- The *suvat* equations from M1.
- The acceleration due to gravity, g, is vertically downwards and is usually taken to be $9.8 \, \text{m s}^{-2}$ (or sometimes $10 \, \text{m s}^{-2}$), from M1.
- Resolving vectors from M1.
- Quadratic equations from C1.

K KEY FACTS

- Projectile motion is usually considered in terms of horizontal and vertical components – the convention used in this section is to take the upwards direction as positive.

- It is important to decide at the outset where the origin and the axes are.

- Angle of projection = α

  Initial velocity, $\mathbf{u} = \begin{pmatrix} u \cos \alpha \\ u \sin \alpha \end{pmatrix}$

  Initial position, $\mathbf{r}_0 = \begin{pmatrix} x_0 \\ y_0 \end{pmatrix}$

  Acceleration, $\mathbf{a} = \begin{pmatrix} 0 \\ -g \end{pmatrix}$

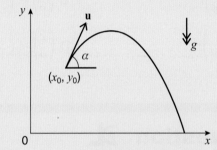

- At time t, velocity, $\mathbf{v} = \mathbf{u} + \mathbf{a}t$

  $$\begin{pmatrix} v_x \\ v_y \end{pmatrix} = \begin{pmatrix} u \cos \alpha \\ u \sin \alpha \end{pmatrix} + \begin{pmatrix} 0 \\ -g \end{pmatrix} t$$

  so $\quad v_x = u \cos \alpha$

  and $\quad v_y = u \sin \alpha - gt$

- At time t, displacement $\mathbf{r} = \mathbf{r}_0 + \mathbf{u}t + \frac{1}{2}\mathbf{a}t^2$

  $$\begin{pmatrix} x \\ y \end{pmatrix} = \begin{pmatrix} x_0 \\ y_0 \end{pmatrix} + \begin{pmatrix} u \cos \alpha \\ u \sin \alpha \end{pmatrix} t + \frac{1}{2}\begin{pmatrix} 0 \\ -g \end{pmatrix} t^2$$

  so $\quad x = x_0 + ut \cos \alpha$

  and $\quad y = y_0 + ut \sin \alpha - \frac{1}{2}gt^2$

Projectiles

EXAMPLE 1

A catapult propels a stone in an upwards direction at an angle θ, where $\cos\theta = \frac{7}{25}$ and $\sin\theta = \frac{24}{25}$, with a speed of 25 m s^{-1} from the top of a vertical cliff which is 36 m above the sea. How long will the stone take to reach the sea? (Take $g = 10$ m s^{-2}.)

SOLUTION

$u_x = u\cos\theta = 25 \times \frac{7}{25} = 7$ and $u_y = u\sin\theta = 25 \times \frac{24}{25} = 24$.

Taking the origin as the point where the cliff meets the sea, and using
$\mathbf{r} = \mathbf{r}_0 + \mathbf{u}t + \frac{1}{2}\mathbf{a}t^2$, this gives $\begin{pmatrix} x \\ y \end{pmatrix} = \begin{pmatrix} 0 \\ 36 \end{pmatrix} + \begin{pmatrix} 7 \\ 24 \end{pmatrix}t + \frac{1}{2}\begin{pmatrix} 0 \\ -10 \end{pmatrix}t^2$

and so $x = 7t$ and $y = 36 + 24t - 5t^2$.

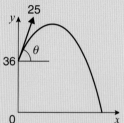

When the stone hits the water, $y = 0$.

That is, $y = 36 + 24t - 5t^2 = 0$.

So $\quad 5t^2 - 24t - 36 = 0$

$\Rightarrow \quad (5t + 6)(t - 6) = 0$

$\Rightarrow \quad\quad\quad\quad t = -1.2$ or 6

As the time cannot be negative, the stone reaches the sea after 6 seconds.

EXAMPLE 2

A particle is projected from the origin with $u_x = 21$ m s^{-1} and $u_y = 21$ m s^{-1}.

i) Find expressions for x and y at time t.

ii) Eliminate t to find the equation of the trajectory.

iii) How far does the particle travel in a horizontal direction when its height is above 20 m? (Take $g = 9.8$ m s^{-2}.)

SOLUTION

i) <u>x direction</u>   <u>y direction</u>

$u_x = 21 \quad a_x = 0$ $u_y = 21 \quad a_y = -9.8$

Using $s = ut + \frac{1}{2}at^2$ in each direction

$x = 21t$ $y = 21t - 4.9t^2$

ii) From the equation for horizontal motion, $t = \dfrac{x}{21}$.

Substituting this value of t in the equation for vertical motion gives

$$y = 21\left(\frac{x}{21}\right) - 4.9\left(\frac{x}{21}\right)^2.$$

This simplifies to give $y = x - \dfrac{x^2}{90}$. ← This is the equation of the trajectory.

iii) When the height is 20 m, $y = 20$

so $20 = x - \dfrac{x^2}{90}$.

Multiplying both sides by 90 and rearranging the terms, this equation simplifies to $x^2 - 90x + 1800 = 0$

$\Rightarrow (x - 30)(x - 60) = 0$, so $x = 30$ or 60.

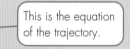

So the particle will travel for 30 m when the height is above 20 m (from $x = 30$ to $x = 60$).

6 Projectiles

EXAMPLE 3

A particle A is projected from the top of a tower which is 12 m high with an initial velocity of $\begin{pmatrix} 15 \\ 15 \end{pmatrix}$ m s^{-1}. At the same moment another particle B is projected from the base of the tower with a velocity of 30 m s^{-1} at an angle of 60° to the horizontal. The trajectories of A and B are in the same vertical plane. Show that the particles collide 1.09 s (3 s.f.) after projection. (Take $g = 9.8$ m s^{-2}.)

SOLUTION

Choose the origin to be at the base of the tower.

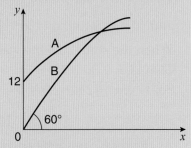

$$u_x = 30 \cos 60° = 15$$
$$u_y = 30 \sin 60° = 25.980...$$

A	**B**
$x_0 = 0 \quad y_0 = 12$	$x_0 = 0 \quad y_0 = 0$
$v_x = 15 \quad v_y = 15$	$v_x = 15 \quad v_y = 25.980...$
$a_x = 0 \quad a_y = -9.8$	$a_x = 0 \quad a_y = -9.8$

Using $\mathbf{r} = \mathbf{r}_0 + \mathbf{u}t + \frac{1}{2}\mathbf{a}t^2$

$$\begin{pmatrix} x_A \\ y_A \end{pmatrix} = \begin{pmatrix} 15t \\ 12 + 15t - 4.9t^2 \end{pmatrix} \text{ and } \begin{pmatrix} x_B \\ y_B \end{pmatrix} = \begin{pmatrix} 15t \\ 25.980... \, t - 4.9t^2 \end{pmatrix}$$

If the two particles collide $x_A = x_B$ and $y_A = y_B$ for the same value of t, that is,

$15t = 15t$ (which is always true) and $12 + 15t - 4.9t^2 = 25.980... \, t - 4.9t^2$

$\Rightarrow \quad\quad 12 + 15t = 25.980... \, t$

$\Rightarrow \quad\quad\quad\quad\quad 12 = 10.980... \, t$

$\Rightarrow \quad\quad\quad\quad\quad\quad t = 1.092...$

So the particles collide 1.09 s (3 s.f.) after they are projected.

A   ADVICE

When solving a question on projectiles it is a good idea to start by
a) drawing a diagram, marking on it the information which you are given
b) finding the equations for v_x, v_y, x and y.

Most questions can then be solved directly by careful use of the diagram and equations.

LINKS

Mechanics   Resisted motion (M4 and DE), Variable mass (M4 and DE).

Test Yourself ▷L

In these questions take the upward direction as positive and $g = 9.8 \, \text{m s}^{-2}$, except where stated otherwise.

1 A small stone is projected horizontally, at $19.6 \, \text{m s}^{-1}$, from a height of $44.1 \, \text{m}$ above horizontal ground. What is the speed of the stone as it hits the ground?

A $\begin{pmatrix} 19.6 \\ -29.4 \end{pmatrix} \text{m s}^{-1}$

B $29.4 \, \text{m s}^{-1}$ in a downwards direction

C $35.3 \, \text{m s}^{-1}$

D $-9.8 \, \text{m s}^{-1}$

2 A particle is projected from ground level with a velocity of $15 \, \text{m s}^{-1}$ at an angle θ, where $\tan \theta = \frac{4}{3}$. For how many seconds is the particle above $7 \, \text{m}$? (Take $g = 10 \, \text{m s}^{-2}$.)

A 1

B 0.4

C 1, 1.4

D It never reaches the height of $7 \, \text{m}$.

3 A pellet is fired from an airgun on the top of a vertical cliff, which is $12 \, \text{m}$ above sea level. The initial velocity of the pellet is $\begin{pmatrix} 7 \\ 22 \end{pmatrix} \text{m s}^{-1}$. How high is the pellet above sea level after $4 \, \text{s}$?

A $28 \, \text{m}$

B $9.6 \, \text{m}$

C $21.6 \, \text{m}$

D $178.4 \, \text{m}$

4 Tower A is $5.78 \, \text{m}$ high and tower B is $5.045 \, \text{m}$ high. They stand $26 \, \text{m}$ apart. From the top of tower A, a rubber bullet is fired horizontally in the direction of tower B with an initial speed of $15 \, \text{m s}^{-1}$. One-tenth of a second later a rubber bullet is fired horizontally from the top of tower B in the direction of tower A with an initial speed of $20 \, \text{m s}^{-1}$. Which one of the following statements is true? Assume that the towers and trajectories of the bullets are all in the same vertical plane.

A The bullets do not collide.

B The bullets collide when the bullet fired from tower B has travelled $12 \, \text{m}$.

C The bullets collide at a height of $2.644 \, \text{m}$ above the ground.

D The bullet fired from tower A reaches the ground first.

Exam-Style Question ▷L

Jack throws a small stone from a point that is 2 m above ground level towards a target that is 15 m away and 7.2 m above ground level. The initial velocity of the stone has horizontal and vertical components of $9 \, \text{m s}^{-1}$ and $12 \, \text{m s}^{-1}$ respectively. (Take $g = 9.8 \, \text{m s}^{-2}$.)

i) Calculate the speed of projection, $u \, \text{m s}^{-1}$, and the angle of projection, θ, of the stone.

ii) Show that, t seconds after the stone has been projected, its height above ground level, y m, is given by the equation $y = 2 + 12t - 4.9t^2$.
   Find the corresponding equation for the horizontal distance, x m.
   Show that the stone misses the target.

Jack tries again to hit the target, this time altering the angle of projection to $45°$, but leaving the speed of projection, $u \, \text{m s}^{-1}$, unchanged.

iii) What are the x and y co-ordinates of the position of the particle after t seconds?
   Show that the equation of the trajectory of the stone is $y = 2 + x - \frac{49}{1125}x^2$. Verify that the stone now hits the target.

iv) At what angle to the horizontal is the stone travelling when it hits the target?

Using components: resultant and equilibrium

A ABOUT THIS TOPIC

When forces act in many directions it is useful to be able to resolve them into components. This section covers the methods you need when using components to find the resultant of several forces or when forces are in equilibrium.

R REMEMBER

- Vector addition and unit vectors from M1.
- Pythagoras' theorem from GCSE and C1.
- Trigonometry ratios: sin θ, cos θ, tan θ. (SOHCAHTOA)
  sin $(90° - \theta)$ = cos θ and cos $(90° - \theta)$ = sin θ from GCSE.
- Newton's first law: Every object continues in a state of rest or uniform motion in a straight line unless it is acted on by a resultant force, from M1.
- When there is no resultant, forces are said to be in equilibrium, from M1.

K KEY FACTS

- When a force is *resolved* into components, a right-angled triangle is used.
  The force is represented by the hypotenuse and the components by the other two sides.

- The first diagram shows a force resolved in horizontal and vertical directions.

$$\mathbf{F} = F \cos \alpha \, \mathbf{i} + F \sin \alpha \, \mathbf{j}$$

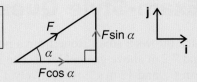

  Notice that the component *adjacent* to the given angle, α, is $F \cos \alpha$ and the component along the *opposite* side is $F \sin \alpha$.

- The second diagram shows the force resolved in two different directions, such as parallel and perpendicular to a plane.

$$\mathbf{F} = F \cos \beta \, \mathbf{i} + F \sin \beta \, \mathbf{j}$$

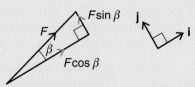

- The force may be replaced by its resolved components.

- The resultant of several forces can be found by resolving them all in the same two perpendicular directions, adding the components and then combining them into a single force using Pythagoras' theorem and trigonometry.

EXAMPLE 1

Two forces **P** and **Q** are shown in the diagram.
P has magnitude 24 N and **Q** has magnitude 15 N.
i) Resolve them in the directions **i** and **j**.
ii) Find the resultant force **P** + **Q**
   a) in component form and
   b) in magnitude and direction form.

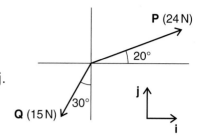

SOLUTION

i) **P** makes an angle of 20° with the **i** direction so its component in that direction is 24 cos 20°.

Its component perpendicular to this in the **j** direction is 24 sin 20°.

P = 24 cos 20° **i** + 24 sin 20° **j**

Q makes an angle of (90° − 30°) = 60° with the negative **i** direction so its component in the **i** direction is −15 cos 60°.

This could equally well be written in terms of the given angle as −15 sin 30°.

Its component in the **j** direction is −15 cos 30° (or −15 sin 60°). Using the given angle:

Q = −15 sin 30° **i** − 15 cos 30° **j**

Notice that you use the cosine of the angle when it is the acute angle between the force and the direction in which you are resolving.

ii) a) Hence **P** + **Q** = 24 cos 20° **i** + 24 sin 20° **j**
            − 15 sin 30° **i** − 15 cos 30° **j**
      = 22.55... **i** + 8.20... **j**
            − 7.5... **i** − 12.99... **j**
      = 15.05... **i** − 4.78... **j**

> Remember to keep the full numbers in your calculator.

This is the component form of **P** + **Q**.

> This is particularly important when finding the direction.

b) First draw a triangle to show the components.

By Pythagoras' theorem, the magnitude of **P** + **Q** is
$$\sqrt{(15.05...)^2 + (4.78...)^2}$$
$$= 15.79...$$

Also tan $\theta = \frac{4.78...}{15.05...}$
$$= 0.317...$$
$$\theta = 17.62...°$$

The magnitude of **P** + **Q** is 15.8 N (3 s.f.) and its direction is 17.6° (3 s.f.) below the **i** direction.

EXAMPLE 2

The diagram shows three forces which are in equilibrium. By resolving in two perpendicular directions, find R and α.

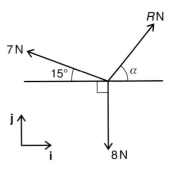

SOLUTION

Let **i** and **j** be unit vectors in the directions shown.
Then resolving in the **i** direction

$$R \cos \alpha - 7 \cos 15° = 0$$
$$R \cos \alpha = 6.761\ldots \qquad \textcircled{1}$$

> 8 N is perpendicular to **i** so has no component in this direction.

In the **j** direction

$$R \sin \alpha + 7 \sin 15° - 8 = 0$$
$$R \sin \alpha = 8 - 1.811\ldots$$
$$R \sin \alpha = 6.188\ldots \qquad \textcircled{2}$$

You can find R by squaring and adding $\textcircled{1}$ and $\textcircled{2}$:

$$R^2(\cos^2 \alpha + \sin^2 \alpha) = 45.71\ldots + 38.29\ldots$$
$$R^2 = 84.012\ldots$$

so
$$R = 9.17 \qquad \text{(3 s.f.)}$$

The angle can be found by dividing $\textcircled{2}$ by $\textcircled{1}$:

$$\tan \alpha = \frac{R \sin \alpha}{R \cos \alpha}$$
$$= \frac{6.188\ldots}{6.761\ldots}$$
$$= 0.915\ldots$$
$$\alpha = 42.5° \qquad \text{(nearest 0.1°)}$$

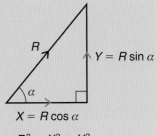

$$R^2 = X^2 + Y^2$$
$$\tan \alpha = \frac{Y}{X}$$

A ADVICE

You will find it useful to remember that $\cos^2 \alpha + \sin^2 \alpha = 1$ and

$$\tan \alpha = \frac{\sin \alpha}{\cos \alpha}$$

EXAMPLE 3

A block of mass 3 kg is sliding down a plane inclined at 20° to the horizontal. There is a frictional force of 5 N. Calculate
i)   the normal reaction between the block and the plane
ii) the resultant force down the plane
iii) the acceleration of the block.

The diagram shows the forces acting on the block. The block's weight is $3g$ N.

i)   Notice that the angle between the normal and the vertical is equal to the angle between the plane and the horizontal. The weight makes an angle of 20° with the normal. The normal reaction is perpendicular to the plane. There is no motion in this direction so the resolved parts balance:

$R = 3g \cos 20°$
$= 27.626...$

The normal reaction is 27.6 N (3 s.f.).

This angle is
$90° - 20° = 70°$
$\cos 20° = \sin 70°$
$\sin 20° = \cos 70°$

ii) The resultant force down the plane is:

$3g \sin 20° - 5$
$= 5.055... $ N

The force down the plane is 5.06 N (3 s.f.).

iii) Using $\mathbf{F} = m\mathbf{a}$
$5.055... = 3a$
The acceleration is $5.055... \div 3 = 1.69$ m s^{-2} (3 s.f.).

LINKS

Mechanics   Newton's laws (M1), Vectors (M1), Projectiles (M1), Forces and motion in two dimensions (M1), General motion (M1), and most of the work covered in later Mechanics units (M2, M3, M4).

Test Yourself

1 The forces in the diagram are in equilibrium.
Three of these statements are false and one is true.
Check each carefully and decide which one is true.

A $F \cos \theta = 7$ B $F \sin \theta = 8 \sin 15°$

C $F^2 = 7^2 + 8^2$ D $F \sin \theta = 8 \cos 15°$

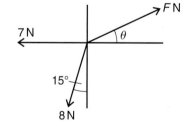

Use the next diagram for **questions 2 to 5**.

2 Three of these statements are true and one is false.
Check each carefully and decide which one is false.

A The resolved component of **P** parallel to **j** is $12 \sin 42°$.

B The resolved component of **Q** parallel to **i** is $34 \cos 28°$.

C The resolved component of **R** parallel to **j** is $46 \cos 18°$.

D The resolved component of **R** parallel to **i** is $46 \sin 18°$.

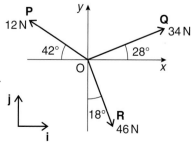

3 Three of these statements are true and one is false.
Check each carefully and decide which one is false.

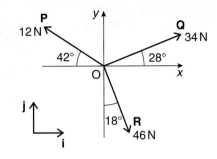

A $P = 12 \cos 42° \, \mathbf{i} + 12 \sin 42° \, \mathbf{j}$

B $Q = 34 \cos 28° \, \mathbf{i} + 34 \sin 28° \, \mathbf{j}$

C $R = 46 \sin 18° \, \mathbf{i} - 46 \cos 18° \, \mathbf{j}$

D $R = 46 \cos 72° \, \mathbf{i} - 46 \sin 72° \, \mathbf{j}$

4 The resultant of the forces **P**, **Q** and **R** is $X\mathbf{i} + Y\mathbf{j}$. Which of these is the value of X?

   A −62.5   **B** 35.3   **C** 53.2   **D** 64.9

5 Which of the following gives the direction of the resultant?

   A 29° to the negative **i** direction above the x axis

   B 29° to the positive **i** direction below the x axis

   C 29° to the negative **i** direction below the x axis

   D 61° to the positive **i** direction below the x axis

Exam-Style Question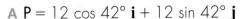

A student is moving a box of books of mass 60 kg along level ground
and then up a ramp to his room. There are two parts to the motion.
First, he pushes it along the rough ground at constant speed with a force
as shown in Fig. 1.

i) Show that the friction force is 130 N and find the normal reaction
with the ground.

Fig. 1

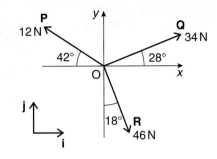

When he reaches the ramp, the student decides to pull the box with a rope
which makes an angle of 35° with the horizontal, as shown in Fig. 2.
The ramp is also rough and makes an angle of 10° with the horizontal.
The friction is now 50 N. The box again travels at constant speed.

ii) Calculate the tension in the rope and the normal reaction with the ramp.

Fig. 2

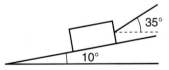

Using Newton's second law in two dimensions

A ABOUT THIS TOPIC

Forces rarely act in the same direction, so this topic covers the methods you need in order to apply Newton's second law when forces act in two dimensions.

R REMEMBER

- Force diagrams from M1.
- Resolving forces from M1.
- Trigonometry ratios, $\sin(90° - \theta) = \cos \theta$, $\cos(90° - \theta) = \sin \theta$ from GCSE.
- Equations for motion with constant acceleration (the *suvat* equations) from M1.

K KEY FACTS

- In two or three dimensions (2-D or 3-D), Newton's second law is used in its *vector* form $\mathbf{F} = m\mathbf{a}$.

- The *acceleration* and the *resultant force* are always in the same direction.

- Problems can be solved by resolving in two perpendicular directions.

- Perpendicular to the acceleration, the components of forces are in equilibrium.

- The equation parallel to the acceleration is often called 'the equation of motion'.

EXAMPLE 1

A boy of mass 35 kg slides down a straight water slide which is 3 m long and inclined at 15° to the horizontal. He starts from rest and the friction is negligible.

i) Find his acceleration and his speed when he hits the water at the end of the slide.

ii) Find the normal reaction of the slide on the boy.

SOLUTION

i) First draw a diagram.

There are two forces acting on the boy: his weight $35g$ N vertically down and the normal reaction with the slide R N. There is no friction.

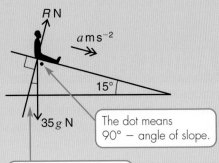

The dot means 90° − angle of slope.

The acceleration a m s^{-2} is parallel to the slide, so it is best to resolve parallel and perpendicular to the slide. The force R N has no component in the direction parallel to the slide.

The angle between the normal and the vertical is 15°. Use sin 15° to resolve down the slide.

The boy's weight makes an angle of $90° - 15° = 75°$ with the slide, so its component down the slide is

$$35g \sin 15° \text{ (or } 35g \cos 75°)$$

Using Newton's second law parallel to the slide gives:

$$35g \sin 15° = 35a$$
$$a = 35g \sin 15° \div 35$$
$$= 9.8 \times \sin 15°$$
$$= 2.536\ldots$$

Now you know $u = 0$, $s = 3$, $a = 2.536\ldots$ and you need v
so use $\quad v^2 = u^2 + 2as$

giving $\quad v^2 = 0 + 2 \times 2.536\ldots \times 3$
$$= 15.218\ldots$$
$$v = 3.901\ldots$$

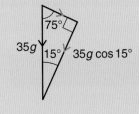

The boy hits the water at about 3.9 m s^{-1} (1 d.p.).
[Notice that **in this case** the mass of the boy (35 kg) cancels out, so the speed should be the same for anyone who uses the slide.]

ii) To find the normal reaction, resolve perpendicular to the slide.
This is perpendicular to the acceleration so the components balance.
$$R = 35g \cos 15° \text{ (or } 35g \sin 75°)$$
$$= 331.312\ldots$$
The normal reaction is 331 N (3 s.f.).

A ADVICE

It is usually best to resolve in directions parallel and perpendicular to the direction of the acceleration. Otherwise, you will have to resolve the acceleration as well.

EXAMPLE 2

Two dog teams are pulling a sledge of mass 120 kg with horizontal forces of 150 N and 300 N as shown in the diagram. The sledge is initially at rest.
There is a resistance of 70 N opposite to the direction of motion of the sledge.
Calculate θ and find the acceleration of the sledge.

What is its speed after 3 seconds?

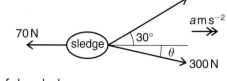

SOLUTION

The diagram shows the components of the forces in the direction of the acceleration and perpendicular to it. The resultant force is parallel to the acceleration so there is no component perpendicular to it.

150 sin 30°

150 cos 30°

70

300 cos θ

300 sin θ

Resolving perpendicular to the acceleration gives:
$$150 \sin 30° = 300 \sin \theta$$
$$150 \times 0.5 = 300 \sin \theta$$
$$0.25 = \sin \theta$$
Hence $\qquad \theta = 14.477...°$

> Use sin θ because you are resolving at right angles to the line adjacent to θ.

Resolving in the direction of motion, the resultant force in newtons is:
$$150 \cos 30° + 300 \cos \theta - 70 = 129.903... + 290.473... - 70$$
$$= 350.376...$$

Using Newton's second law, $350.376... = 120a$
$$a = \frac{350.376...}{120} = 2.919...$$

The acceleration is 2.92 m s^{-2} (3 s.f.).

Now you know $a = 2.919...$, $u = 0$ and after 3 s, $t = 3$.

You need v so use
$$v = u + at$$
$$v = 0 + 2.919... \times 3$$
$$= 8.759...$$

The speed after 3 s is 8.76 m s^{-1} (3 s.f.).

EXAMPLE 3

A 3.5 kg block, A, lies on a rough slope inclined at 10° to the horizontal. It is attached to a light, inextensible string which passes over a smooth pulley at the top of the slope. Another block, B, of mass 2.5 kg, hangs vertically from the end of the string.
The system is held at rest and then released and it is found that block A takes 2 seconds to slide 1.5 m up the slope.
i) Calculate the acceleration of the system.
ii) There is a frictional force F N between A and the slope. Find F.

SOLUTION

i) When solving problems like this you have two strategies for finding an acceleration. One is to use $\mathbf{F} = m\mathbf{a}$, the other is to use the constant acceleration equations. In this question you are told a lot about the motion, so use the second strategy.

You know $u = 0$, $t = 2$, $s = 1.5$ and you need a.

Use
$$s = ut + \tfrac{1}{2}at^2$$
$$1.5 = 0 + \tfrac{1}{2}a \times 2^2$$

Giving $1.5 = 2a$

The acceleration is 0.75 m s^{-2}.

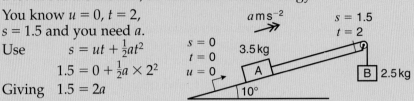

ii) Now you can use $\mathbf{F} = m\mathbf{a}$.

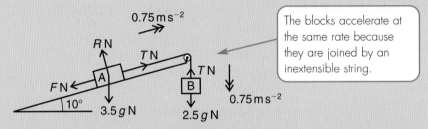

The blocks accelerate at the same rate because they are joined by an inextensible string.

First draw a diagram showing all the forces. As well as the weights of the blocks and the friction force F N acting on A, there is a tension force of T N in the string. It is the same throughout because the pulley is smooth.

The acceleration of A is up the slope and the acceleration of B is vertically downwards. Because they are moving in different directions, you cannot treat A and B as a single object. Use Newton's second law in the direction of motion for each of the blocks separately. Resolve vertically for B and parallel to the slope for A.

For B, vertically **down**: $2.5g - T = 2.5a$ ①
You know $a = 0.75$ so $\quad 2.5g - T = 2.5 \times 0.75$
$$T = 2.5g - 2.5 \times 0.75$$
$$T = 22.625$$

For A, **up** the slope:
$$T - F - 3.5g \sin 10° = 3.5a \quad ②$$
$$22.625 - F - 5.956\ldots = 3.5 \times 0.75$$
$$22.625 - 5.956\ldots - 2.625 = F$$
$$14.044\ldots = F$$

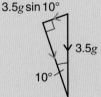

The frictional resistance is 14.0 N (3 s.f.).

Alternatively, you can eliminate T from ① and ② by adding them and hence find F.

LINKS

Mechanics   Constant acceleration equations (M1), Newton's laws (M1), Vectors (M1), General motion (M1), and most of the work covered in the later Mechanics units (M2, M3, M4).

Test Yourself ▷L

1 Forces of 12 N and 20 N at 60° to each other act on a 2.5 kg object. Use the method of resolving forces to find the magnitude of the acceleration of the object.

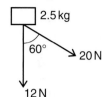

    A $11.2\,\mathrm{m\,s^{-2}}$ **B** $11.1\,\mathrm{m\,s^{-2}}$ **C** $10.4\,\mathrm{m\,s^{-2}}$ **D** $8.8\,\mathrm{m\,s^{-2}}$

2 Two children of mass 25 kg and 40 kg are racing down identical water slides which each make an angle of 30° to the horizontal. They both start at rest in identical positions. Three of these statements are true and one is false. Which one is false?

    A If there is no frictional force the result is a draw.

    B If the frictional force is 10 N on each, the heavier child wins.

    C If the frictional force is 0.01 × the weight of the child, the result is a draw.

    D If the frictional force is 0.1 × the weight of the child, the lighter child wins.

Use the following information to answer **questions 3 and 4**.

A climber of mass 50 kg is being pulled up from a ledge by a rope which is pulled through a pulley as shown in the diagram. The pulley is smooth, so the tension in the rope is the same on both sides.
The climber is accelerating upwards at $0.3\,\mathrm{m\,s^{-2}}$.

Before you answer these questions, draw a diagram showing the tension, TN, in the rope, the weight of the climber and her acceleration.

3 Calculate the tension in the rope.

    A $T = 65\,\mathrm{N}$ **B** $T = 490\,\mathrm{N}$ **C** $T = 505\,\mathrm{N}$ **D** $T = 637\,\mathrm{N}$

4 Find the magnitude and direction of the force of the rope on the pulley. Three of these statements are true and one is false. Which one is false?

    A Its horizontal component is 414 N.

    B Its vertical component is 795 N.

    C The resultant force is 466 N.

    D The resultant makes an angle of 62.5° with the downward vertical.

Exam-Style Question ▷L

A block of mass 12 kg slides down a rough slope which is inclined at 5° to the horizontal.
The block starts with a speed of 1.5 m s⁻¹ at the top of the slope and it is assumed that there is a constant resistance to motion of 15 N.

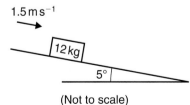

(Not to scale)

i) Calculate the acceleration of the block.

ii) For how long does the block slide down the slope? How far does it travel?

iii) Measurements show that the block actually comes to rest in 3.5 s.
There is an error caused by assuming the resistance is 15 N.
Calculate the true value of the resistance.

Triangle of forces

When two forces act on an object or three forces are in equilibrium, it is often useful to approach the problem by drawing a triangle. This section is about using this method.

- Vector addition from M1.
- Trigonometry ratios and $\sin(180° - \theta) = \sin\theta$ from GCSE.
- The cosine rule and the sine rule from GCSE.

- Triangles are commonly used to represent forces in two *different* ways.
- The **resultant** of two forces is represented by the third side in a nose-to-tail diagram.

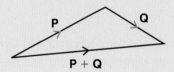

- When an object is in *equilibrium* under the action of three forces F_1, F_2 and F_3 they can be represented in magnitude and direction by a **triangle of forces**.

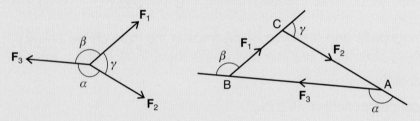

The resultant of two forces

When finding the resultant of two forces, an alternative to using components is to solve the vector triangle. The resultant of **P** and **Q** can be found by first drawing the vector triangle.

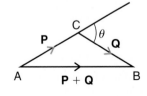

> This works in a similar way to displacing an object. Moving it from A to C to B has the same result as moving it directly from A to B.

The forces **P** and **Q** should be parallel to two sides of the triangle **taken in order** (A to C to B) and then the resultant is parallel to the third side (A to B).

EXAMPLE 1

Two forces **P** and **Q** are shown in the diagram.
P has magnitude 24 N and **Q** has magnitude
15 N.

i)   Draw a diagram to illustrate their resultant
     P + **Q**.

ii) Hence find the magnitude and direction
     of the resultant.

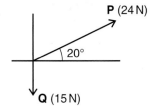

SOLUTION

i)   Start by drawing **P** and **Q** following in
     order A-B-C, then join AC. This
     represents the resultant **P** + **Q**.
     You don't have to do it accurately, but
     the sides and angles should look the
     right size.

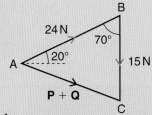

ii) This triangle is not right-angled and you know two
     sides and the included angle, so you need to use the cosine rule:

$$b^2 = a^2 + c^2 - 2ac \cos B$$

giving: $b^2 = 15^2 + 24^2 - 2 \times 24 \times 15 \times \cos 70°$
$$= 225 + 576 - 720 \times \cos 70°$$
$$= 801 - 246.254\ldots$$
$$= 554.745\ldots$$

so $b = 23.553\ldots$

The magnitude of the resultant is 23.6 N (3 s.f.).

You can now use the sine rule to find the angle A.

$$\frac{\sin A}{a} = \frac{\sin B}{b}$$

So $\sin A = \dfrac{15 \sin 70°}{23.553\ldots}$

$$= 0.598\ldots$$

So the angle A = 36.8° (nearest 0.1°).

Therefore **P** + **Q** is 23.6 N and is at an angle of
36.8° − 20° = 16.8° below the horizontal.

Triangle of forces

When three forces **P**, **Q** and **R** are in equilibrium, **P** and **Q** can be replaced
by their resultant **P** + **Q**. This means that the third force **R** must balance
that resultant and so **R** = −(**P** + **Q**). It must be the same magnitude but in
the opposite direction. The three forces can be represented by the sides of
a triangle taken in order. This is the *triangle of forces*.

The next example illustrates how triangles of forces can be used as an
alternative method to answer questions similar to those you have met in
the previous section.

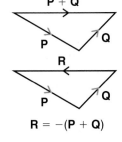

EXAMPLE 2

A bird feeder of mass 1.6 kg is hanging on a
washing line using a smooth hook. One side
of the line makes an angle of 20° to the
horizontal. Calculate the tension in the washing line.

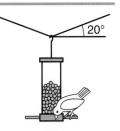

SOLUTION

The hook is smooth, so the tension (T N) is the same both sides.

The triangle of forces ABC is therefore isosceles, so the problem can be solved using symmetry.

In the diagram $\quad AD = DB = \frac{1}{2} \times 1.6g$
$$= 0.8g$$

In triangle DBC $\quad \sin 20° = \dfrac{0.8g}{T}$

$$T = \dfrac{0.8g}{\sin 20°}$$

The tension in the washing line is 22.9 N (3 s.f.).

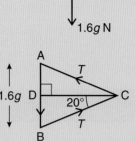

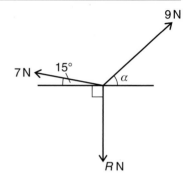

EXAMPLE 3

The diagram shows three forces which are in equilibrium.
Use the triangle of forces to find α and R.

SOLUTION

The forces are in equilibrium so can be represented by the sides of a triangle taken in order. In this triangle you know the sides a, b and the angle A, so use the inverted sine rule first to find angle B.

$90° - 15° = 75°$

$$\frac{\sin B}{b} = \frac{\sin A}{a}$$

$$\sin B = \frac{7 \sin 75°}{9}$$

$$= 0.751\ldots$$

so $\quad$ angle B = 48.7° (nearest 0.1°)

You should consider $180° - 48.7°$ as a possible solution, but clearly B < A, because $b < a$.

and $\quad$ angle C = $180° - (75° + 48.7°)$
$$= 56.3° \text{ (nearest 0.1°)}.$$

Thus $\quad \alpha = 56.3° - 15°$
$$= 41.3° \text{ (nearest 0.1°)}.$$

To find R use the sine rule.
$$\frac{R}{\sin 56.3°} = \frac{9}{\sin 75°}$$

$$R = \frac{9 \sin 56.3°}{\sin 75°}$$

$$= 7.751\ldots = 7.75 \text{ N (3 s.f.)}.$$

This is quite like the situation in example 2 on page 58. You could apply the triangle of forces to that question too, solving it by using similar methods to those in example 1 here.

LINKS

Pure Mathematics
Solving triangles
(C2).

Mechanics
Vectors (M1),
Forces and motion
in two dimensions
(M1),
General motion
(M1),
Situations when
bodies are in
equilibrium (M2,
M3, M4).

Test Yourself ⊃L

1 Two young husky dogs are pulling a sledge on smooth ground. Each dog is pulling with a force of 90 N, one in a northerly direction and the other in an easterly direction. The mass of the sledge is 75 kg.
Draw two diagrams, one to show the forces on the sledge and the other a triangle to find the resultant force. Calculate the resultant force and hence find the magnitude (to 2 s.f.) and direction of the acceleration of the sledge.

   A $1.2\,\mathrm{m\,s^{-2}}$ in the direction NE   B $1.2\,\mathrm{m\,s^{-2}}$ in the direction SW
   C $1.7\,\mathrm{m\,s^{-2}}$ in the direction NE   D $1.7\,\mathrm{m\,s^{-2}}$ in the direction SW

2 The diagram shows a container being loaded onto a ship using two ropes OP and OQ. The mass of the container is 5500 kg and the forces are in equilibrium.
Draw a diagram for yourself showing the forces acting at O and then draw a triangle of forces. Use this to calculate the tensions in the ropes OP and OQ.
Three of the following statements are true and one is false. Which one is false?

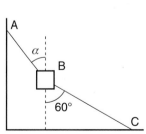

   A The triangle of forces is isosceles.

   B The tensions in the two ropes are equal.

   C The tension in OP is 53.9 kN.

   D The tension in OQ is 88.3 kN.

The following information refers to **questions 3 and 4**.

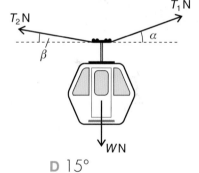

A cable car of weight W N is attached to a cable which is moving with a constant velocity. The two parts of the cable have tensions T_1 and T_2 and make angles α and β with the horizontal as shown.

3 In one position $\alpha = 15°$ and $T_2 = 6W$.
Use the triangle of forces to calculate β.

   A $-5.7°$ B $4.8°$ C $9.3°$ D $15°$

4 In a different position $T_1 = 8W$, $T_2 = kW$ and $\alpha = 20°$. Draw a triangle of forces with W N represented by 1 unit, $8W$ N by 8 units etc. Use this to find k and hence find T_2.

   A $8.4W$ B $7.7W$ C $7.5W$ D $4.1W$

Exam-Style Question ⊃L

A small box of weight 400 N is held in equilibrium by two light strings AB and BC. The ends C and A are fixed so that BC is at 60° to the vertical. AB makes an angle α to the vertical where $\alpha < 60°$.

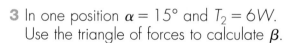

  i) Draw a labelled diagram showing all the forces acting on the box.

  ii) In one situation AB is fixed so that $\alpha = 30°$.
     By drawing a triangle of forces, calculate the tensions in BC and AB.

  iii) Show carefully, but briefly, that the box cannot be in equilibrium if $\alpha = 60°$ while BC remains at 60° to the vertical.

General motion

8

Motion using calculus

A ABOUT THIS TOPIC

You have already studied motion in a straight line where the acceleration is constant. You will now be using calculus to answer similar questions in more general cases where the acceleration is not necessarily constant and may be expressed as a function of time.

R REMEMBER

- The language of kinematics and the basic definitions from M1.
- The use of position–time, velocity–time and acceleration–time graphs from M1.
- The calculus techniques, such as differentiation to find a gradient and stationary points, and integration to find the area under a graph, from C2.
- The curve-sketching techniques from C1 and C2.
- The area between a velocity–time curve and the t axis represents displacement. This is often referred to as 'the area under the graph'. When v is negative, the displacement is negative.
- Areas of the regions between an acceleration–time curve and the t axis represent changes in velocity; when a is negative the change in velocity is negative.

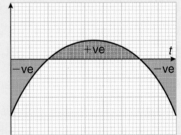

For regions above the t axis, the areas are taken to be +ve.
For regions below the t axis, the areas are taken to be −ve.

K KEY FACTS

- In this section, the displacement s, the **instantaneous** velocity v and the **instantaneous** acceleration a of a particle moving in a straight line are all taken to be functions of time t.

displacement	velocity	acceleration

Differentiate $\longrightarrow$

$$s \qquad\qquad v = \dfrac{\mathrm{d}s}{\mathrm{d}t} \qquad\qquad a = \dfrac{\mathrm{d}v}{\mathrm{d}t} = \dfrac{\mathrm{d}^2s}{\mathrm{d}t^2}$$

Integrate $\longleftarrow$

$$s = \int v\,\mathrm{d}t \qquad\qquad v = \int a\,\mathrm{d}t \qquad\qquad a$$

- When you find velocity from acceleration, or displacement from velocity, you use integration and so an arbitrary constant is involved. You need more information to find this constant but it is not needed if you use definite integration (that is, integrate between limits).

> ⚠ If you are given an expression for s, v or a in terms of t, only use the *constant acceleration* (*suvat*) formulae when you are **sure** that the acceleration is constant.

A ADVICE

Be sure that you know the language of kinematics. Especially important are the distinctions between: *displacement* and *distance travelled*; *velocity* and *speed*.

If in the slightest doubt, draw a sketch graph: position–time, velocity–time, distance–time, etc.

Examples 1–5 are about a particle, P, that moves along the x axis where the unit of length is the metre. Its velocity, v m s^{-1}, at time t seconds is given by $v = 12t^2 - 6t - 6$, where $-1 \leqslant t \leqslant 1$. When $t = -1$, $x = 3$.

> Notice that all the units are S.I.

Acceleration

EXAMPLE 1

Find an expression in terms of t for the acceleration, a m s^{-2}, of the particle P at time t.

SOLUTION

$v = 12t^2 - 6t - 6$

Differentiating, $a = \dfrac{dv}{dt} = 24t - 6$.

EXAMPLE 2

i) Draw the velocity–time graph for P for $-1 \leqslant t \leqslant 1$.
ii) Find the greatest and least values of the velocity of P for $-1 \leqslant t \leqslant 1$.

SOLUTION

i)

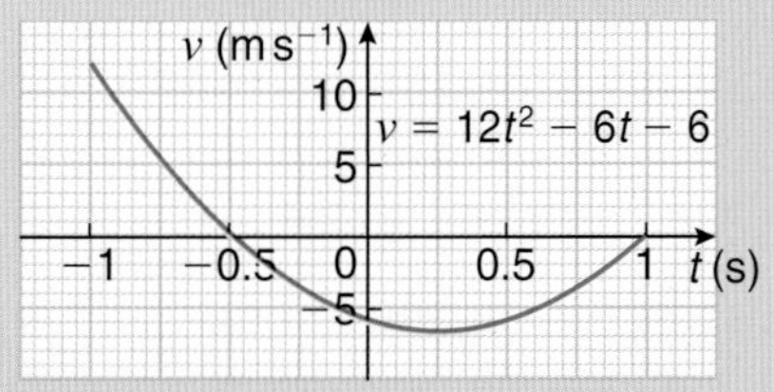

> Greatest and least values in an interval are either at the ends or at a maximum or minimum point. The graph shows that the greatest value is at the left-hand end-point and that the least value is inside the given interval $-1 \leqslant t \leqslant 1$.

ii) The greatest value is when $t = -1$
so is given by $v = 12 \times (-1)^2 - 6 \times (-1) - 6 = 12$.
Thus the greatest velocity is 12 m s^{-1}
(speed of 12 m s^{-1} in the direction Ox).

For the least value you need $a = 0$.
This occurs when $24t - 6 = 0$ and
so $t = 0.25$.

> The least value of v occurs when $a = 0$. Since $a = \dfrac{dv}{dt}$, this is equivalent to finding a stationary point.

When $t = 0.25$
$v = 12 \times 0.25^2 - 6 \times 0.25 - 6 = -6.75$

> The −ve sign shows that the motion is in the opposite direction to Ox.

The least velocity is -6.75 m s^{-1} (speed 6.75 m s^{-1} in the opposite direction to Ox).

Position

EXAMPLE 3

Find an expression for the position of P at time t.

SOLUTION

> *x* is used because the *position* is being found.

$$x = \int (12t^2 - 6t - 6)\,\mathrm{d}t$$

$$= 12 \times \frac{t^{2+1}}{3} - 6 \times \frac{t^{1+1}}{2} - 6 \times \frac{t^{0+1}}{1} + C$$

$$= 4t^3 - 3t^2 - 6t + C$$

> Remember that $x = 3$ when $t = -1$.

Now use the information that $x = 3$ when $t = -1$ to find C.

$3 = 4 \times (-1)^3 - 3 \times (-1)^2 - 6 \times (-1) + C$

so $3 = -4 - 3 + 6 + C$ and $C = 4$

Thus $x = 4t^3 - 3t^2 - 6t + 4$.

EXAMPLE 4

What is the position of P when its velocity is instantaneously zero?

SOLUTION

> You could use the quadratic formula instead of factorising.

When $v = 0$, you have $12t^2 - 6t - 6 = 0$

$6[2t^2 - t - 1] = 0$

> Start by taking out the common factor 6.

$\Rightarrow 6[2t^2 - 2t + t - 1] = 0$

$\Rightarrow 6[2t(t - 1) + 1(t - 1)] = 0$

$\Rightarrow 6(2t + 1)(t - 1) = 0$

$\Rightarrow t = -0.5$ or $t = 1$

> Look at the velocity–time graph in example 2. This also tells you when $v = 0$ and indicates it is when $t = -0.5$ or $t = 1$.

You already know from example 3 that the expression for the position of P is

$x = 4t^3 - 3t^2 - 6t + 4$.

When $t = -0.5$

$x = 4 \times (-0.5)^3 - 3 \times (-0.5)^2 - 6 \times (-0.5) + 4 = 5.75$

When $t = 1$

$x = 4 \times 1^3 - 3 \times 1^2 - 6 \times 1 + 4 = -1$

The positions are 5.75 m and -1 m.

Displacement

Displacement is the difference between one position and another. When you use the word you must also specify the starting position or time; for example, 'the displacement from point A' or 'the displacement from its position at time $t = 1$'. Displacement from the origin is the same as position.

EXAMPLE 5

Find the displacement of P from its position when $t = -1$ to its position when $t = 1$.

SOLUTION

You already know from example 3 that the expression for the position of P is $x = 4t^3 - 3t^2 - 6t + 4$.

When $t = 1$ $x = 4 - 3 - 6 + 4 = -1$

When $t = -1$ $x = -4 - 3 + 6 + 4 = 3$

So the displacement from its position when $t = -1$ to its position when $t = 1$ is $(-1) - (3) = -4$ m.

Displacements may be found directly as areas under a graph without finding positions first. Look at the velocity–time graph for P. This has been shaded to indicate the displacement from $t = -1$ to $t = 1$ with the region above the t axis shown in black and that below it in red to emphasise that these represent +ve and −ve displacements, respectively. The overall displacement is the sum of the **signed** areas of these regions. The process of integration automatically gives the areas the correct signs.

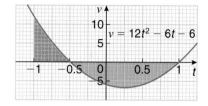

> Notice that you do not have enough information to find an expression for the position.

Examples 6–8 are about a particle, Q, that moves along the x axis. The unit of length is the metre. Its velocity, v m s^{-1}, at time t seconds is given by $v = 18t - 3t^2 - 24$ where $0 \leqslant t \leqslant 4.5$.

EXAMPLE 6

i) Draw the velocity–time graph for Q for $0 \leqslant t \leqslant 4.5$.

ii) Find an expression in terms of t for the displacement of Q from its position when $t = 1$.

iii) Use your answer to part **ii)** to find the displacement of Q from its position when $t = 1$ to its position when $t = 3$.

SOLUTION

i)

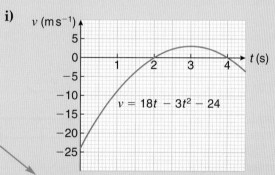

> Notice the change in notation:
> s for displacement,
> x for position.

ii) Let the displacement of Q from its position when $t = 1$ be s.
When $t = 1$, the displacement is zero and so $s = 0$.

Now find $s = \int (18t - 3t^2 - 24)\, \mathrm{d}t$, where $s = 0$ when $t = 1$.

Integrating, you get $s = 9t^2 - t^3 - 24t + C$.

Putting $s = 0$ when $t = 1$ gives $0 = 9 - 1 - 24 + C \Rightarrow C = 16$.

The required expression is $s = 9t^2 - t^3 - 24t + 16$.

iii) Now you just need to find the value of s when $t = 3$.

The required displacement is
$9 \times 3^2 - 3^3 - 24 \times 3 + 16 = 81 - 27 - 72 + 16 = -2$
so it is -2 m.

> The −ve sign shows that the total displacement is in the opposite direction to Ox.

A | ADVICE

Always show how you evaluate an arbitrary constant. There will almost always be marks for doing this, even when its value is clearly zero.

Look at examples 5 and 6. In both you find the displacement from position at one time to position at another.

- In example 5 you already had an expression for the position, x, at time t and so you used it to find the displacement.
- In example 6 you did not have an expression for the position so you first found one for the displacement from the position when $t = 1$ and then you used it.
- A further method, definite integration, is shown in example 7. This is used when you have only been asked for the displacement from the position at one time to the position at a later time.

The 'best' method depends on what information you have and what expressions you have already found.

Using definite integration

EXAMPLE 7

Find the displacement of Q from its position at $t = 1$ to its position at $t = 3$.

SOLUTION

The lower limit 1 is the start time.
The upper limit 3 is the end time.

The displacement is given by

$$s = \int_1^3 (18t - 3t^2 - 24) \, dt$$

$$= [9t^2 - t^3 - 24t]_1^3$$

$$= (9 \times (3)^2 - (3)^3 - 24 \times (3)) - (9 \times (1)^2 - (1)^3 - 24 \times (1))$$

so $s = (-18) - (-16) = -2$ and the displacement is -2 m, as found in example 6.

> It often useful to name the integrated function $F(t)$. In this case $F(t) = 9t^2 - t^3 - 24t$. The value of the integral is expressed as $F(3) - F(1)$.

Distance travelled

In example 7 you were asked to find the displacement of Q between $t = 1$ and $t = 3$. In example 8 you will be asked to find the distance travelled between those times. To understand the difference, look at this diagram. It indicates displacements along the x axis.

at $t = 2$, $v = 0$ m s^{-1} at $t = 1$, $v = -15$ m s^{-1}

at $t = 3$, $v = 3$ m s^{-1}

You can infer the main features of the diagram from the velocity–time graph. (The graph seems to show that $v = 0$ when $t = 2$ and this may be confirmed by solving $v = 0$.)

- Between $t = 1$ and $t = 2$, the velocity is in the negative direction and the displacement from A to B is negative.
- At $t = 2$, the velocity is zero.
- Between $t = 2$ and $t = 3$, the velocity is in the positive direction and the displacement from B to C is positive.

The **displacement** is represented by the distance AC in the negative direction.

The **distance travelled** is the distance AB + the distance BC.

$v = 18t - 3t^2 - 24$

EXAMPLE 8   Find the distance travelled by Q between $t = 1$ and $t = 3$.

SOLUTION

As you can see from the diagram on the previous page there are two parts to the journey, from A to B and from B to C. You first find the displacements for each part.

$$AB: \int_1^2 (18t - 3t^2 - 24) \, dt = [9t^2 - t^3 - 24t)]_1^2$$
$$= (-20 - (-16)$$
$$= -20 + 16 = -4$$

$$BC: \int_2^3 (18t - 3t^2 - 24) \, dt = [9t^2 - t^3 - 24t)]_2^3$$
$$= (-18 - (-20)$$
$$= -18 + 20 = 2$$

Travelling from A to B is a distance 4 m in the negative direction and travelling from B to C is a distance 2 m in the positive direction, so the distance travelled is $4 + 2 = 6$ m.

A ADVICE

If you need displacement as well as distance travelled, it is easiest to work the problem as in example 8. Having found the displacement from A to B to be -4 m and the displacement from B to C to be 2 m, the **displacement of Q** is $(-4) + 2 = -2$ m; the **distance travelled** by Q is $|-4| + |2| = 4 + 2 = 6$ m.

> The symbol | | (called the modulus) means that the +ve value is taken.

LINKS

Pure Mathematics   Applications of calculus (C2, C3, C4, DE, FP2).
Mechanics   Applications of calculus (M3, M4).

Test Yourself ▷L

1 A toy is moving in a straight line and its velocity at time t seconds is v m s^{-1}, where $v = -4t^2 + t + 5$ for $-1 \leqslant t \leqslant 3$. When is the acceleration of the toy zero?

   A $t = 0$

   B $t = 0.125$

   C $t = -0.125$

   D $t = -1$ and $t = 1.25$

2 A particle of grit, G, is stuck to the top of a piece of machinery that is moving up and down a vertical y axis. The height of G above the ground is y metres at time t seconds where $y = 10t - 2t^2 - 8$. Determine the direction of motion and speed of G when $t = 3$.

   A Downwards, 2 m s^{-1}

   B Downwards, -2 m s^{-1}

   C Upwards, 2 m s^{-1}

   D Upwards, 4 m s^{-1}

3 A particle is moving in a straight line and t seconds after passing through a point A its velocity is V m s^{-1}, where $V = 4t - t^2 - 1$ for $0 \leqslant t \leqslant 5$. Draw a velocity–time graph before you start to answer the question. Use it to help you decide which one of the following contains only true statements.

A Initially the velocity of the particle is -1 m s^{-1} and its acceleration is 4 m s^{-2} so the displacement of the particle from A after 3 seconds is 15 m.

B The initial velocity of the particle is -1 m s^{-1} and its velocity after 3 seconds is 2 m s^{-1} so the displacement of the particle from A after 3 seconds is 1.5 m.

C The speed of the particle after 1 second is twice its initial speed; its greatest speed is 3 m s^{-1}.

D The particle does not always travel in the same direction; its greatest velocity is $+3$ m s^{-1}.

In **questions 4 and 5**, an insect is moving along an x axis. At time t seconds, its velocity is v m s^{-1}, where $v = 30t - 3t^2 - 63$.

4 Calculate the displacement of the insect from its position when $t = 2$ to its position when $t = 4$.

  A -2 m   B 2 m   C -150 m   D -76 m

5 Calculate the distance travelled by the insect in the time interval $2 \leqslant t \leqslant 4$.

  A 157 m   B 12 m   C -2 m   D 2 m

Exam-Style Question DL

A particle moves along the x axis with velocity v m s^{-1} at time t seconds given by $v = 18t - 12 - 6t^2$.

i) Find an expression for the acceleration of the particle at time t.

ii) Find the times t_1 and t_2, where $t_1 < t_2$, at which the particle has zero velocity.

iii) Find the distance travelled between the times t_1 and t_2.

iv) At time t_1 the particle passes through the point A. Does the particle pass through A on any later occasion? At time t_2 the particle passes through the point B. Does the particle pass through B on any later occasion?

v) Find the distance travelled from $t = 0$ to $t = 3.5$.

Motion in two and three dimensions

A | ABOUT THIS TOPIC

You have already studied motion in a straight line with constant acceleration and acceleration that varies with respect to time. In this section you have to apply the ideas met in earlier sections (pages 1, 10, 70) to a **vector** representing displacement, velocity or acceleration in two or three dimensions.

R | REMEMBER

- The language of kinematics and the basic definitions, covered in M1 and the first section of this guide.
- The use of *suvat* equations from M1.
- Vector notation and the techniques for finding the magnitude and direction of a vector in two dimensions and the magnitude of a vector in three dimensions from M1.
- The use of calculus to study general motion in a straight line, covered in M1 and in the previous section.
- Position vectors are written in two dimensions as $\mathbf{r} = x\mathbf{i} + y\mathbf{j}$ or $\mathbf{r} = \begin{pmatrix} x \\ y \end{pmatrix}$

  and in three dimensions as $\mathbf{r} = x\mathbf{i} + y\mathbf{j} + z\mathbf{k}$ or $\mathbf{r} = \begin{pmatrix} x \\ y \\ z \end{pmatrix}$

  where $\mathbf{i}$, $\mathbf{j}$ and $\mathbf{k}$ are the standard unit vectors.

K | KEY FACTS

- In this section, the displacement $\mathbf{s}$, the instantaneous velocity $\mathbf{v}$ and the instantaneous acceleration $\mathbf{a}$ of a particle moving in a straight line are all taken to be functions of time t.

  displacement   velocity   acceleration

  Differentiate →

  $$\mathbf{s} = x\mathbf{i} + y\mathbf{j} = \begin{pmatrix} x \\ y \end{pmatrix} \qquad \mathbf{v} = \frac{d\mathbf{s}}{dt} = \dot{x}\mathbf{i} + \dot{y}\mathbf{j} = \begin{pmatrix} \dot{x} \\ \dot{y} \end{pmatrix} \qquad \mathbf{a} = \frac{d\mathbf{v}}{dt} = \ddot{x}\mathbf{i} + \ddot{y}\mathbf{j} = \begin{pmatrix} \ddot{x} \\ \ddot{y} \end{pmatrix}$$

  ← *Integrate*

  $$\mathbf{s} = \int \mathbf{v}\, dt \qquad \mathbf{v} = \int \mathbf{a}\, dt \qquad \mathbf{a}$$

  > The dot notation (called Newton's notation) is an alternative notation to use when differentiating with respect to time.

- For constant acceleration, $\mathbf{v} = \mathbf{u} + \mathbf{a}t$ $\mathbf{r} = \mathbf{r}_0 + \mathbf{u}t + \frac{1}{2}\mathbf{a}t^2$ $\mathbf{r} = \mathbf{r}_0 + \mathbf{v}t - \frac{1}{2}\mathbf{a}t^2$
  $\mathbf{r} = \mathbf{r}_0 + \frac{1}{2}(\mathbf{u} + \mathbf{v})t$

- For constant mass, Newton's second law is $\mathbf{F} = m\mathbf{a}$.

- The direction of the motion of a particle is the direction of its velocity and **not** of its position.

It is usually better to work in the column vector form than in the **i**, **j**, **k** form; this includes cases when the question is given in terms of **i**, **j**, **k** or the answer is required in that form. Column vectors allow you to see all of the **i** components in the top row, all of the **j** components in the second row and, if there is a third dimension, all of the **k** components in the third row.

Constant acceleration

Examples 1–3 are about a particle, P, with acceleration $(5\mathbf{i} - 3\mathbf{j})\,\text{m s}^{-2}$. The time is t seconds. When $t = 0$, P is at O with velocity $(-3\mathbf{i} + 4\mathbf{j})\,\text{m s}^{-1}$. The unit vectors **i** and **j** have directions east and north respectively.

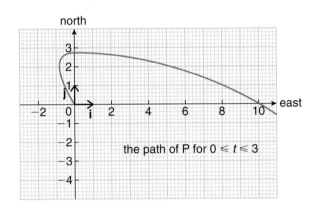

the path of P for $0 \leqslant t \leqslant 3$

EXAMPLE 1

Find the speed of P when $t = 3$.

SOLUTION

Since the acceleration is constant (both **i** and **j** components are constant), you can use $\mathbf{v} = \mathbf{u} + \mathbf{a}t$ with $t = 3$, $\mathbf{u} = \begin{pmatrix} -3 \\ 4 \end{pmatrix}$ and $\mathbf{a} = \begin{pmatrix} 5 \\ -3 \end{pmatrix}$.

This gives $\mathbf{v} = \begin{pmatrix} -3 \\ 4 \end{pmatrix} + 3\begin{pmatrix} 5 \\ -3 \end{pmatrix} = \begin{pmatrix} -3 + 15 \\ 4 - 9 \end{pmatrix} = \begin{pmatrix} 12 \\ -5 \end{pmatrix}$

> The working is done using column vectors.

The speed of P is the magnitude of **v** so it is $\sqrt{12^2 + (-5)^2} = 13\,\text{m s}^{-1}$.

> The formula has been used as $\mathbf{u} + t\mathbf{a}$ as you usually write the scalar multiplier in front of the vector.

EXAMPLE 2

Find the direction of motion of P when $t = 0.6$, giving your answer as a bearing.

SOLUTION

The direction of motion of P is the direction of its velocity.
Using $\mathbf{v} = \mathbf{u} + \mathbf{a}t$ with $t = 0.6$ gives

$\mathbf{v} = \begin{pmatrix} -3 \\ 4 \end{pmatrix} + 0.6\begin{pmatrix} 5 \\ -3 \end{pmatrix}$

$= \begin{pmatrix} -3 + 3 \\ 4 - 1.8 \end{pmatrix} = \begin{pmatrix} 0 \\ 2.2 \end{pmatrix}$

$\mathbf{v} = 2.2\mathbf{j}$ so **v** is in the +ve **j** direction which is due north, bearing 000°.

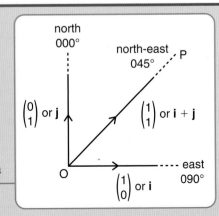

EXAMPLE 3

How long after passing through O is P north-east of O?

SOLUTION

The position of P relative to O is **s**,
the displacement from O.
Using $\mathbf{s} = \mathbf{u}t + \frac{1}{2}\mathbf{a}t^2$ gives

$$\mathbf{s} = t\begin{pmatrix} -3 \\ 4 \end{pmatrix} + \frac{t^2}{2}\begin{pmatrix} 5 \\ -3 \end{pmatrix} = \begin{pmatrix} -3t + 2.5t^2 \\ 4t - 1.5t^2 \end{pmatrix}.$$

When P is north-east of O, the **i** and
j components of its position are
equal and positive.
$-3t + 2.5t^2 = 4t - 1.5t^2$
$\Rightarrow 4t^2 - 7t = 0$
and this gives $t(4t - 7) = 0$ so $t = 0$
or $t = 1.75$.

P is at O when $t = 0$ and when $t = 1.75$,
P is at $(2.40625\mathbf{i} + 2.40625\mathbf{j})$ m (equal and positive components), so it
is north-east of O after 1.75 seconds.

A ADVICE

There is more
about directions in
the section 'Vector
notation' and in
the Test Yourself
Q2 answer notes.

north
000°

north-east
045° P

$\begin{pmatrix} 0 \\ 1 \end{pmatrix}$ or **j** $\begin{pmatrix} 1 \\ 1 \end{pmatrix}$ or **i + j**

east
090°

O $\begin{pmatrix} 1 \\ 0 \end{pmatrix}$ or **i**

Non-constant acceleration

EXAMPLE 4

The position vector of a bee, **r** m, at time t s is given by
$\mathbf{r} = 12\mathbf{i} + (6t^2 + 3)\mathbf{j} + (2t - 3)\mathbf{k}$. Is the velocity ever zero?

SOLUTION

$$\mathbf{r} = \begin{pmatrix} 12 \\ 6t^2 + 3 \\ 2t - 3 \end{pmatrix}. \text{ Now } \mathbf{v} = \dot{\mathbf{r}} = \begin{pmatrix} 0 \\ 12t \\ 2 \end{pmatrix}.$$

Hence **v** is never zero.

For a vector to be zero **all** its components must be **simultaneously** zero.
Look at **v**. The **i** component is always zero, the **j** component is zero
when $t = 0$, the **k** component is never 0.

As $x = 12 \Rightarrow \dot{x} = 0$,
$y = 6t^2 + 3 \Rightarrow \dot{y} = 12t$,
and $z = 2t - 3 \Rightarrow \dot{z} = 2$.
(Note how the 'dot'
notation saves space.)

EXAMPLE 5

A small bird has velocity $\begin{pmatrix} 2 \\ 7 \end{pmatrix}$ m s^{-1}, when $t = 1$ and acceleration,

a m s^{-2}, given by $\mathbf{a} = \begin{pmatrix} 2t + 4 \\ 3t^2 - 2t + 3 \end{pmatrix}$ for $0 \leqslant t \leqslant 2$, where t is the time

in seconds.
Find an expression for the velocity, **v** m s^{-1}, of the bird at time t.
Find also the velocity of the bird when $t = 2$.

SOLUTION

Since $\mathbf{v} = \int \mathbf{a}\, dt$, $\mathbf{v} = \begin{pmatrix} \int(2t + 4)dt \\ \int(3t^2 - 2t + 3)dt \end{pmatrix}$

Hence $\mathbf{v} = \begin{pmatrix} t^2 + 4t + C \\ t^3 - t^2 + 3t + D \end{pmatrix}$

> Notice that integrating $\mathbf{a}$ means that you integrate each component separately. Each component has an arbitrary constant and you must not assume they are the same.

Using the information that $\mathbf{v} = \begin{pmatrix} 2 \\ 7 \end{pmatrix}$ when $t = 1$ gives

$\begin{pmatrix} 2 \\ 7 \end{pmatrix} = \begin{pmatrix} 1^2 + 4 \times 1 + C \\ 1^3 - 1^2 + 3 \times 1 + D \end{pmatrix} = \begin{pmatrix} 5 + C \\ 3 + D \end{pmatrix}$ so $\begin{cases} 2 = 5 + C \text{ and } C = -3 \\ 7 = 3 + D \text{ and } D = 4 \end{cases}$

Hence $\mathbf{v} = \begin{pmatrix} t^2 + 4t - 3 \\ t^3 - t^2 + 3t + 4 \end{pmatrix}$.

When $t = 2$,

$$\mathbf{v} = \begin{pmatrix} 2^2 + 4 \times 2 - 3 \\ 2^3 - 2^2 + 3 \times 2 + 4 \end{pmatrix} = \begin{pmatrix} 9 \\ 14 \end{pmatrix}$$

so the velocity is $\begin{pmatrix} 9 \\ 14 \end{pmatrix}$ m s^{-1}.

The path of an object

EXAMPLE 6

The position vector of a particle at time t is given by
$\mathbf{r} = (t - 1)\mathbf{i} + (t - 2t^2 + 3)\mathbf{j}$. Find the cartesian equation of its path and plot the graph for $-1 \leqslant x \leqslant 3$.

SOLUTION

Referred to the axes Ox and Oy, $\mathbf{r} = x\mathbf{i} + y\mathbf{j}$.
In this question, $\mathbf{r} = (t - 1)\mathbf{i} + (t - 2t^2 + 3)\mathbf{j}$
and so $x = t - 1$ and $y = t - 2t^2 + 3$.

> The expression for x is simpler than that for y, and so is the one used to make t the subject.

You now eliminate t.

Make t the subject of $x = t - 1$, giving $t = x + 1$.

Substituting for t in $y = t - 2t^2 + 3$ gives

$\begin{aligned} y &= (x + 1) - 2 \times (x + 1)^2 + 3 \\ &= x + 1 - 2(x^2 + 2x + 1) + 3 \\ &= 2 - 3x - 2x^2 \end{aligned}$

> This is the cartesian equation of the curve.

so $y = 2 - 3x - 2x^2$.

Substituting values for x gives the points $(-1, 3)$, $(0, 2)$, $(1, -3)$ and $(2, -12)$.
Now plot the graph.

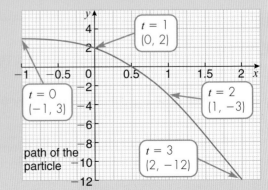

path of the particle

An important and easy alternative way to obtain this graph is to plot co-ordinates (x, y) for different values of t.

> You can use this method when you can't make t the subject of either of the expressions for x and y.

t	$x = t - 1$	$y = t - 2t^2 + 3$	(x, y)
0	−1	3	(−1, 3)
1	0	2	(0, 2)
2	1	−3	(1, −3)
3	2	−12	(2, −12)

LINKS

Pure Mathematics   Vectors (C4), Parametric equations (C4).

Test Yourself ▷L

1 One end of a kite string is held at a fixed point O, the origin of position vectors. The other end P is attached to the kite. The position vector, $\mathbf{r}$ m, of P at time t seconds is given by $\mathbf{r} = (3 - t)\mathbf{i} + (7 + t^2)\mathbf{j} + (t^3 - 2t^2 + 3)\mathbf{k}$. The unit vectors $\mathbf{i}$, $\mathbf{j}$ and $\mathbf{k}$ are in the directions Ox, Oy and Oz with $\mathbf{i}$ and $\mathbf{j}$ horizontal and $\mathbf{k}$ vertical. The kite string is taut at all times. Verify that $x = 0$ when $t = 3$. At this time, what is the length and angle of elevation of the kite string?

A 20 m; about 53°

B 20 m; about 37°

C 16 m; about 53°

D 16 m; about 37°

2 A boat has position vector, $\mathbf{r}$ km, at time t hours given by
$\mathbf{r} = \begin{pmatrix} 2t^3 - 9t^2 + 12t + 3 \\ 3t^2 - 2t^3 - 3 \end{pmatrix}$, where $\begin{pmatrix} 1 \\ 0 \end{pmatrix}$ and $\begin{pmatrix} 0 \\ 1 \end{pmatrix}$ are in the directions east and north, respectively, for $0 \leqslant t \leqslant 2$. The origin of position vectors is at O, the position of a small buoy.

Which of the following statements about the motion of the boat is (completely) true?

A The time $t = 1$ is not the only time when it is stationary.

B When $t = 2$ it is travelling south-east.

C When $t = 0$ it is $3\sqrt{2}$ km from O, travelling east.

D When $t = 2$ it is north-west of O.

3 The acceleration of a toy car, $\mathbf{a}$ cm s^{-2}, is given by $\mathbf{a} = \begin{pmatrix} 8 \\ 6t^2 - 2t + 1 \end{pmatrix}$ at time t seconds.

Its velocity is $\begin{pmatrix} 3 \\ -1 \end{pmatrix}$ cm s^{-1} when $t = 2$. Find its velocity when $t = 3$.

A $\begin{pmatrix} 6 \\ 48 \end{pmatrix}$ cm s^{-1}

B $\begin{pmatrix} 5 \\ 48 \end{pmatrix}$ cm s^{-1}

C $\begin{pmatrix} 5 \\ 33 \end{pmatrix}$ cm s^{-1}

D $\begin{pmatrix} 5 \\ 20 \end{pmatrix}$ cm s^{-1}

4 A particle is at $\begin{pmatrix} 0 \\ -1 \end{pmatrix}$ m with velocity $\begin{pmatrix} 2 \\ 3 \end{pmatrix}$ m s^{-1} when $t = 1$. Its constant acceleration is $\begin{pmatrix} -2 \\ 4 \end{pmatrix}$ m s^{-2}. Find its position when $t = 4$.

A $\begin{pmatrix} -3 \\ 26 \end{pmatrix}$ m

B $\begin{pmatrix} 0 \\ 28 \end{pmatrix}$ m

C $\begin{pmatrix} -8 \\ 43 \end{pmatrix}$ m

D $\begin{pmatrix} 6 \\ 8 \end{pmatrix}$ m

Exam-Style Question

At time t seconds, a toy boat has velocity $\mathbf{v}$ m s^{-1} given for $-1 \leqslant t \leqslant 2$ by $\mathbf{v} = (2t - 2)\mathbf{i} + (2t + 2)\mathbf{j}$, where $\mathbf{i}$ and $\mathbf{j}$ are unit vectors east and north. The origin of position vectors is O and the position vector of the boat is $(-\mathbf{i} + 2\mathbf{j})$ m when $t = 1$.

i) Find the acceleration of the boat at time t.

ii) On what bearing is the boat travelling when $t = 0.5$?

iii) Determine the times (if any) when the boat moves due north.

iv) Determine the times (if any) when the boat is south-west of O.

v) Determine the times (if any) when the boat is (instantaneously) at rest.

Index

Formulae and results

Here are some formulae and results which you will need to recall or derive for the M1 examination. There is an underlying assumption that students already know all the results needed for GCSE Mathematics. The following list is not exhaustive, and you should check with your teacher before your examination.

Constant acceleration formulae

Written in scalars $s = ut + \frac{1}{2}at^2$ $s = \frac{1}{2}(u + v) \times t$ $s = vt - \frac{1}{2}at^2$

$v = u + at$ $v^2 - u^2 = 2as$

Written in vectors $\mathbf{s} = \mathbf{u}t + \frac{1}{2}\mathbf{a}t^2$ $\mathbf{s} = \frac{1}{2}(\mathbf{u} + \mathbf{v})$ $\mathbf{s} = \mathbf{v}t - \frac{1}{2}\mathbf{a}t^2$

$\mathbf{v} = \mathbf{u} + \mathbf{a}t$

(There is no simple vector equivalent of $v^2 - u^2 = 2as$.)

General motion

Written in scalars $v = \dfrac{\mathrm{d}s}{\mathrm{d}t} = \dot{s}$ $s = \displaystyle\int v\,\mathrm{d}t$

$a = \dfrac{\mathrm{d}v}{\mathrm{d}t} = \dot{v} = \dfrac{\mathrm{d}^2s}{\mathrm{d}t^2} = \ddot{s}$ $v = \displaystyle\int a\,\mathrm{d}t$

These results can also be written using vectors; in that case the symbol $\mathbf{r}$ is often used instead of $\mathbf{s}$ for displacement.